THE GRASS IS NEVER GREENER

The grass is never greener

The hilarious adventures of a family
in search of the perfect place to live

ROBERT THOMAS ALLEN

Illustrated by
Paul Galdone

THE BOBBS-MERRILL COMPANY, INC.
Indianapolis   New York

TO WIN AND MUNROE FISHER

AUTHOR'S NOTE

WHENEVER my search for the Perfect Place to Live ended with my family crying in a swamp, I usually came out of it with an idea for an article on domestic disharmony which I suggested to *Maclean's* magazine and usually got okayed. Other times, the idea came from the other direction, originating with *Maclean's* and reaching me in desert, mountain or palmetto or in an area surrounded by Gifte Shoppes. Either way *Maclean's* kept my supply lines open for many years, and from these articles came the basis of what follows. When this book is off the press, wherever I am, I'm going to let off a lot of firecrackers, pinwheels and exploding stars in gratitude to *Maclean's* editors and staff. I'm going to send up some rockets, too, for *Canadian Home Journal*, which also tracked me down with many similar welcome assignments.

ROBERT THOMAS ALLEN

THE GRASS IS NEVER GREENER

1

ONE winter night in my native city of Toronto, Canada, I came home from work after an hour-and-a-half struggle with snow, slipping wheels and snarled traffic and announced to my wife:

11

"This settles it! This is it! I'm finished! All the sunny countries in the world, why we gotta live like Eskimos? We're going to California. Year-round good climate. Oranges a dime a dozen. And you need a blanket at night."

Next day it was clear and crisp, and the traffic had all started again. I felt good. When I got home, I asked my wife if she'd like to go to a movie.

"I can't," she said. "I'm busy getting ready."

"You going somewhere?" I asked.

She turned slowly, frowning at an old tweed jacket of mine that she was holding up as if she were getting ready to waltz with it. She bit her lip thoughtfully and, without taking her eyes off the coat, said, "Are you ever going to wear this again? We won't have much room in our luggage as it is."

"Where we going?"

"To California, of course," my wife said.

I squinted at her sideways. "You been sitting under a drier too long or something?" I'd completely forgotten my outburst of the night before. "When are we going to California?"

My wife turned and faced me, shoulders trimmed and chin held high, ready to hold her own against any male malarky. She looked at me levelly out of dauntless blue eyes, under which she had gone a scrappy pink.

"Do you mean to stand there and say you don't remember telling me last night we were going to live in California?"

"For the love of Pete," I said, remembering. "All I said was that I didn't like blizzards."

My five-year-old daughter, Jane, a solemn, fat-chopped little blonde with a wisp of white hair bobby-pinned to a

12

tiny pink bow, moved up beside her mother and faced me.

"I'm on Mummy's side," she said, her little bow quivering with loyalty.

Her sister, Mary, a fast, happy, darker, two-year-old version with a rollicking belly laugh, stopped running long enough to join the group.

"You said we were going somewhere for a blanket," she said, loyal but confused.

They all confronted me like a pioneer family who had just found out I'd been selling liquor to the Indians.

"You *said* we were going to California," my wife told me.

I had, of course. But what I couldn't explain to three women was that this is the sort of thing that men do all day at work without anyone's taking it seriously. Whenever a guy downtown gets bored, he just says to anyone who will listen something like this:

"Welp! This is it. I'm going to quit my job, borrow ten thousand dollars and open up a little motor court somewhere. Maybe Great Bear Lake."

His office mate looks out the window at some pigeons on a roof across the street and says thoughtfully, "It might go, George. This country is still short of good motor courts. Did I tell you what I was thinking of doing? There's another expedition starting for Mount Everest, and they need an accountant. Thought I'd look into it. I'm in a rut."

Neither of them ever mentions this conversation again. There's a sort of code among men that you never hold them to anything they say they're going to do, any more than you'd expect a ballet dancer to spend the rest of her life with one leg in the air just because you caught her doing her exercises. Enthusiasm for enthusiasm's sake is a form of recreation known to all men.

13

But men probably would never get anything done if they didn't occasionally get enthusiastic around women, who take everything seriously, especially putting ideas into action. When my wife realized that I had just been having a sort of psychological exercise, she hung my coat back in the closet and put the whole thing down to something else about me that she hadn't figured on when she got married. But she had given me a brisk mental shove that kept me trotting along in a new direction. Maybe we *should* move to a warmer climate. It started me thinking. Obviously she was ready to go with me. I began to see that this thing could be reality.

A few nights later I mentioned it again. My wife eyed me patiently. "I thought you said you didn't mean it."

"I didn't—I mean, well I meant it in a way—but I didn't really mean it. But I've been wondering—maybe California isn't the place but——" I pulled out a weather map I'd picked up that day. "Look, do you know how little sunshine we get in Toronto in a year?"

It was the beginning.

Starting with the weather, my wife and I became convinced that somewhere there was a better world. We didn't know how it was colored or shaped or where it was. The only thing we knew about it was that it wasn't the one we were in. It was the ideal place to live, and we were destined, somehow, to get there.

I had a steady job in an advertising office. We had a nice home, a circle of friends, good health and reasonable expectations of untroubled old age. Everything was fine, but we decided everything could be even better in another place—someplace with a perfect climate.

We became so conscious of the weather that it became our chief topic of conversation. We read booklets and learned the amount of sunshine required to prevent rickets and the ideal humidity for human health. My wife, who was in her element again now that there was some action taking place, read weather reports aloud, snapping out the statistics as if she were bringing me in for a landing. "Precipitation, two and a half; hours of sunshine, three and a half; slight fog in the forenoon."

It's surprising how important a thing becomes when you look at it long enough. The weather became something tangible to hang our troubles on, and we talked about it so much that we got others talking about it. If formed the focal point of a minor school of philosophy among our friends, who thought people should do the things they *wanted* to do and go the places they wanted to go, instead of living like mice.

"I was reading today that you can live for as little as three dollars a week in Montevideo," somebody would say after a game of bridge and a late snack at our house. Or maybe it would be Tombstone or Phoenix or Lima. Anyway it was someplace none of us had been. "Three dollars a week! Imagine! I was just saying to Norma on the way over tonight, 'What keeps us from pulling up stakes and going to a place like that?'"

One of our friends, a tall, enthusiastic young insurance salesman, was particularly inspiring. "Do you know why we live such narrow lives?" he'd say. "Because we're like sheep. Because we think that just because everyone else does, we have to live like this——"

He'd break off to indicate my living room with a sweeping gesture, put an olive in his mouth, sit back, with the olive making a lump as if he had his tongue in his cheek, and go on.

"Why do we do it? Why crowd into cities and scrabble for money? All a man really needs is some little shack in the mountains or on the sea. He wouldn't have luxuries, maybe. No movie a block away or department store around the corner. But, by God, he'd be doing the things he wanted to do."

Still starry-eyed with ideas about life in a little shack, he'd slip into his heated car and go back to his tile bathroom, electric refrigerator and oil-heated bedroom and forget the whole thing. But not me. Nor my wife. We really believed it. Finally we reached that why-do-we-just-*talk*-about-it-why-don't-we-*do*-it? stage, and I came up with a doozer of an idea.

Ever since I'd left school, I'd wanted to be a writer. I'd spent my nights and week ends at it and got nowhere, probably because all my plots were solved either by a house catching on fire or a bad storm. But I figured it was because I didn't have enough time at my writing. If I could just get a crack at it full time, I thought, I'd make it go.

Now I saw a neat way of doing this and at the same time moving to the Perfect Place to Live. I got out a pad and pencil. A lot of disasters start with a clean white pad and a sharp pencil. I could sell my house at a profit of about $3,000. That would be plenty to launch me as a writer. It was true that this was an artificial profit, because I'd have to pay proportionately more for another house. But this was the beauty of the whole thing—I wouldn't need to buy another house. Not until inflated values subsided,

16

anyway. As a self-employed writer, I could live anywhere (I thought). I'd have a chance that others didn't have. I could live in places that were impractical for wage earners, where, accordingly, the housing and rental situation would be a lot easier. We could find someplace with a perfect climate. We could see a bit of the world at the same time. My elder daughter, Jane, hadn't started school; Mary wouldn't be going for some time. And—well, everybody knew that travel was wonderful for children—so educational.

Or look at it this way. We could live for a year at least on the three thousand dollars, even if I didn't sell a thing (chuckle). This trip was to be sort of a reconnaissance. We'd come back to Toronto in the spring, think things over in the light of our trip and definitely make up our minds about where we were going to live. So even if the whole idea turned out to be a flop, and we came home and bought another house, and I got another job, what, in effect, would have taken place? We'd simply have sold our house and bought another one. I'd have changed jobs. When you got right down to it, we would have just taken a little longer to move than most people, going by way of, for instance, New Mexico. There were other arguments which escape me now.

The argument I'd overlooked, of course, was that we would have spent about $3,000 on a trip, that I'd be out of work, that we wouldn't have a home, and, as subsequently happened, that real estate values would keep going up— in fact, they haven't come down yet. Also there was that matter about my making *some* money in a year. It's amazing how long you can go without making money at writing,

17

especially when you write short stories that end with houses catching on fire.

We began getting bundles of literature from various chambers of commerce, looking for some place free of snow, ice, frost, fog and, by a simple extension of our enthusiasm, of congestion, unpleasant people, barking dogs and boredom. One bundle of publicity included a map that divided the continent into hours of sunshine instead of states and provinces. The sunnier the climate, the lighter the shading on the map, and right in the southwest corner of the United States, straddling the California-Arizona state line, there was a pure white spot about the size of a large pea where it never rained and which began to symbolize for us perfect bliss. It was only eight inches on my map, which isn't far when you're looking at it over a toasted cheese sandwich, and from where we sat you couldn't see the sand or the snow on the mountains.

I had a 1934 Chevrolet with bucket seats and running boards that I'd bought for $400. I hadn't intended to keep it, but just to use it as a trade-in on a better car, but it ran so beautifully that I decided we might as well use it for our trip across the continent.

We decided that while we were at it, we'd see the rest of the country. I mean, for all we knew maybe Florida would be the Perfect Place to Live, and it would be foolish to drive right past it. So, as we became fond of saying, we'd load up the old jalopy and just head off in the general direction of the South. We could live just anywhere, in a little shack in the mountains or a little shack beside the sea, all those places that people with jobs can't move to (although we found that they use them to throw old tires and beer cans in) . There was no rush about deciding where to

18

live. After all, we wanted it to be just right. If we liked a place, we'd stay around for awhile. And if the car broke down (heh heh), what of it? We'd still have $3,000. We'd sell the car, hop the nearest train, and just keep going. What a life!

2

THIS was at a time when people were given to saying with a knowing nod, "It's a seller's market." The buyer was someone forced by circumstances to pay outlandish prices and criminal down payments. And here I was with a house to sell. Brother! I lived in a brick bungalow in North Toronto. I put the house on the market with a classified ad, and for the next few nights, when the supper dishes were cleared away, I'd smooth out a paper napkin, lick the end of a pencil and sit there figuring out my profits and squirming greedily as I got richer.

But soon I almost ran out of napkins, and the only thing that had happened was that all the other newspapers had phoned telling me that I should try them. I began sitting around our living room trying to hear the faint stir of a classified ad at work, a sound so inaudible that I developed a slight squint. I did that for two months. I soon stopped thinking of the real estate situation in terms of a deserving but homeless buyer forced to pay my price. I discovered that for every buyer there's a seller just as broke and just as worried. He deals in thousands of dollars he never owned and ends up studying a complicated report called "Disbursements and Statement of Adjustments" and trying to figure out what shrunk his profits.

But I learned a lot of things about selling a house which I'm willing to pass on to anyone who may be interested. The first thing to get into your head if you're going to sell your house is that the best prices for houses are being paid when you're trying to buy one. When you try to sell yours, nobody wants one, especially one with the down payment you have to get. This economic law apparently doesn't apply to your friends, who all sell houses just like yours for twice as much as they cost. Furthermore, they have so many customers the first night the ad runs that they almost have to call the cops to shoo leftover buyers off the lawn. I can't explain this. All I know is that if your experience is anything like mine, you'll get three customers.

One will be a middle-aged woman named Mrs. May, who glances around your house vaguely then sits in your favorite chair till suppertime, telling you a long story about her husband, who had a hernia two years ago and hasn't been any good since. At five minutes to six she'll look at her watch and say she must scoot.

Another will be a man named Morrison, who has thin black hair combed sideways and a brisk way of going through your house like a bus driver at the end of a run. Every time you apologize for anything, he laughs in a friendly way and says it doesn't matter, as he's going to knock the walls down anyway, move the fireplace over to the other end of the living room and put a breakfast nook where your bookcase is. You'll never see him again, unless someday you happen to be selling another house.

Around about the fifth week you'll have a visit from a sad, plump little man with no eyebrows who walks around the outside of the house kicking the wall and whispering to a tall, thin friend he brings with him. The last time I saw him he got me out of a hot bath, where I'd been lying trying to figure out how to get my house out of the exclusive hands of a real estate man who had evidently moved to Europe. I came out clutching a bathrobe around me and followed him around peering at him through the steam on my glasses, like a river pilot in a fog. I stood around anxiously kicking everything he kicked. We all ended up in my bedroom gently kicking the baseboard. He walked out with thoughtfully lowered head, got into a truck and drove away.

Another thing, don't make the mistake at any point during the selling of your house of sitting back and saying, "Well, I've got the law on my side." Nobody ever has the law on his side but the lawyers. Any time I've ever said, "I have the law on my side," I've found myself fighting desperately to keep out of jail. One time during the rental mix-up after the war, before I owned a house, I checked with a man at the Rentals Administration of the Wartime Prices and Trade Board about whether I had to get out of my house by a certain date. He kept saying, "You're safe as a church." I ended up being threatened with charges of holding, resisting, stalling, contempt of court and everything but insanity, and finally had to move everything I owned, including a firmly bolted workbench weighing about half a ton, in twenty-four hours.

Signing an offer to purchase is the turning point in selling your house. It's a long legal form that is to a real estate man what an order blank is to a brush salesman. Everybody signs it, including you. The buyer makes out a check for a deposit of, say, five hundred dollars. This shows his good faith and is held, along with his good faith, pending the closing date, when you adjust all charges, like the gas bill. You turn over the key. You all smile and shake hands. You go ahead with your other arrangements—buying a new house or a ticket to Tahiti. You tell all your friends that you've sold your house. You've made a deal—unless the buyer decides he was only kidding.

I got an offer to purchase from a fat, chuckling man in an expensive-looking, pin-striped suit. My wife and I sat down and said, "Whew! Well, it's all over at last!" We went out that night and had lobster Newburg. A week later I was trying to get the fat man to stop hanging up on me when I phoned him. A rumor had reached me through the real estate man that he wasn't going to buy my house after all.

I couldn't just run out and cash his check, because he'd stopped payment on it, and, besides, I didn't have it. I think the real estate man had it as a token of somebody's good faith. Anyway I was concentrating on making the customer buy the whole house, not just five hundred dollars' worth of it. I said to my wife, "Well this is it! He asked for it. It's his problem. I'll take it easy if he has children."

I phoned the lawyer I'd intended to have handle the deal. I said, "When do we start dragging this man through every court in the land?"

"You sure you got the right number?" the lawyer said. "This is a lawyer's office."

"I *know* it's a lawyer's office. That's what I want. Look, this guy buys my house, signs an offer to purchase then just decides to change his mind about the whole thing. When do we slap him with everything in the book?"

"Mr. Allen," the lawyer said wearily, "I've given this my considered opinion."

"What's your plan?" I asked, baring my teeth at myself in the hall mirror.

"Drop it," he said.

"Drop it!" I yelped. "Whaddaya mean, *drop* it! We've got him on six carbon copies, three witnesses, the Small Loans Act, the short form, the long form and a check."

"Allen," the lawyer kept saying quietly, "drop it."

He was right, of course. It would have meant two years just to get the case *into* the courts, let alone get it out. It would have been fun only if I'd been a millionaire with a hobby of long legal chess games.

You can see how hopeless it is, anyway, trying to make somebody buy something. All he needs to say is that he

24

doesn't want it. He can tell you that he hasn't any money and go to Bermuda, which is where you thought you'd be.

And, take it from me, the law won't have anything to do with anything hopeless when it comes to a showdown. The law will have very little to do with anything when it comes to a showdown. If there's anything a lawyer hates, it's getting tangled up with the law.

In the meantime, although the buyer was tentatively tied to my house, so was I. In other words, I couldn't sell it to someone else, because the fat man could still change his mind and start payment on the check, and I would suddenly be in the position of trying to sell my house to one person after I had a deposit and an offer to purchase from another.

Once I phoned the customer's lawyer about it. He said, "Look, Allen, my client hasn't been *entirely* unreasonable. After all, you misrepresented your mortgage, your down payment, interest, lot number, frontage and your wife's middle name." When I told my lawyer about it, he implied that if I would lie low he might be able to get me off.

It ended with my going to the buyer's lawyer and getting what is known as a release, or the customer's permission to sell my own house to somebody else. I thought for awhile he wasn't going to let me. If that's legal revenge, you can have it.

You're going to find yourself dealing with real estate men too. Maybe you'll strike a good one. But there's also a chance that you'll strike a few like one I got, a freckled little Irishman who advertised himself as Good Deal McGuire and who lived in the country and raised Holsteins as a hobby. He ran billboards all over town showing one of

25

his prize Holsteins, with the caption, "Don't Be Bull-headed: Let McGuire Handle It." One of McGuire's men came up to the house, went around making notes and finally said, mysteriously, "Look, Mr. Allen, there's one little thing that I'd like to get straight right now. Do you mind *how* we sell your house?"

"Uh—how do you mean?" I said.

He winked. "Well, McGuire is an old-line circus man, and when he starts beating those publicity drums, well!—" he chuckled — "things move! It's just that his methods are a bit unorthodox. I like to get an okay from the client first."

I thought happily of blimps being moored to my chimney or maybe Miss Canada sitting on my doorstep trying on nylons. I lowered my voice and said conspiratorially, "After all, we *both* want to sell the house, don't we?"

Then McGuire moved behind the iron curtain. My wife and I sat waiting for the blimps. I'd read somewhere a few tips on selling a house. One was to leave all the lights on to make it cheery, and the other was to keep it neat and polished. By the end of the month the only caller we'd had was Mrs. May. My head was sunburned from the glare of the lamps, and we'd rubbed the furniture till we almost had holes in the end tables. Finally I phoned McGuire.

"This is Allen," I said.

"Who?"

"Allen."

"You want to buy a house or something?"

"Look, I'm selling a house."

"Sorry. Nobody wants them. You haven't got a second-hand vacuum cleaner, have you?"

"For the—! McGuire, *you're selling a house for me.* Allen, my name is. Six-room bungalow with a corner window."

"Oh *that* Mr. Allen." He began to talk like a football announcer. "We're doing all we can, Mr. Allen. We're pushing it. We're shoving it. I'm advertising it extensively. I have six salesman banging away at it. Been thinking up a little promotion scheme. Your cash payment is a bit high, but I think we can move it."

It turned out that his wild promotion scheme was a sign that he'd had his son letter placed in his window. It read, DON'T PASS UP THIS JIM DANDY BARGAIN, but somebody had shoved a geranium in front of it.

I took my house away from Good Deal McGuire and gave it to a real estate man named Fairplay, a former used car salesman from Vancouver, who got another offer to purchase for me. This house of mine was right in the city, and I don't know how it became connected with cows, but this customer was a technician in a government breeding station, a broody young man with brown sideburns, gold-rimmed glasses and a built-in blush which gave him a permanent expression of having been insulted. I found out later that he was a friend of Fairplay.

Instead of kicking my furnace, he kept asking about my neighbors. My neighbor to the west was a middle-aged man with a small face and a mustache. He always wore a black homburg and stood motionlessly in his garden for hours, hands clasped behind his back, smoking a cigar in the dead center of his mouth. I've seen him stand that way beside a pile of burning leaves for most of a week end. I had no idea what kind of man he was. As a result, whenever my customer asked me about my neighbors, I bore down on the one on the other side, a weather-beaten, soft-

27

spoken man with tragic brown eyes, a courtly manner, three noisy sons, a daughter who was studying drama, two rabbits and a mania for making pickles. The first words he ever spoke to me were, "Do you like pickles?" He told me with quiet confidence that he was going to make a pickle man out of me and that he'd made pickle men of lots of men who didn't like pickles. He chuckled as he cited cases of indigestion he had caused. He had pickles down in his cellar—pickled tomatoes, German pickles, dill pickles, sweet pickles, sour pickles and a laundry tub full of sauerkraut.

I told my customer he was one of the best neighbors I'd ever had, which was the truth. I was extremely fond of the whole family. I added that he was a fine Christian man who you wouldn't know was around the house, as he worked as a machinist on a Toronto Harbour ferry at night and slept all day. He would have been sleeping, too, if a load of coal he'd ordered hadn't arrived just as my customer was mooching around my back yard, sniffing nervously, winking one eye and asking if my neighbors were all right.

It was during the days of wartime shortages, and the coalman pointed out to my neighbor that there was a law that the coal was supposed to be delivered to the nearest cellar window.

I heard my neighbor say, "Well, I knew you fellas were getting pretty independent, but—" he cleared his throat gently—"surely to Christ you wouldn't dump a load of coal on top of a man's laundry tubs, would you?"

The coalman looked at him as if he were trying to sabotage the country. He said that rules were made for everybody and that he wasn't paid to worry about laundry tubs.

28

It was the one and only time I saw my neighbor lose his temper. He swore for what seemed to me, and I suppose to my customer, about five minutes and ended up by kicking an empty garbage pail right out onto the street.

The next I heard of my customer was from his lawyer, who said his client had changed his mind. I went down to Fairplay's office. It was a couple of minutes before I realized that a man up a ladder painting the outside of the frame office building was Fairplay himself, who ignored me. All he'd say was, "I'm busy. See my lawyer."

If a man's up a ladder and won't come down, there's very little you can do about it, but this was sometimes hard to explain to lawyers during the following weeks.

"Why didn't you talk to the real estate man?" they'd say.

"Couldn't get him down off the ladder," I'd explain.

"I don't... quite... understand. Off a *ladder?* What has that to do with a real estate man?"

"I don't know *what* it has to do with a real estate man," I'd say. "I'm just telling you, he was up a ladder and wouldn't come down."

"Why didn't you get another ladder?" they'd say, humoring me.

A month later, in desperation, I knocked off a thousand dollars and, two weeks later, sold the house to a man from North Bay who looked at me sideways and said moodily that he guessed everybody had to get used to paying twice what everything was worth.

I secretly agreed with him and actually felt a bit sorry for the poor sucker for having to pay so much more for the house than I'd paid for it three years earlier, when all I'd done was to build a new veranda on it, paint the inside and the outside, wallpaper every room, move a radiator weighing about a ton to the back of the house and one at the back to the front, build a new fence around the whole property, sledge-hammer a trench in the cellar, lay tile in it to drain a low spot and cement it over again. But I afterward found out that a year later he painted the front steps and sold the house for four thousand dollars more than he paid me for it.

OPERATION Sunshine was now really under way. Although it was much too early in the season for cottage life in Canada, we had planned to stay until the fall at a summer resort seventy miles east of Toronto before leaving for the South. As the house was now sold, we decided that we could manage somehow to get through the remaining four or five weeks of spring weather at a cottage. I quit my job, and we sold our furniture and rented a box trailer to handle the disposition of a few remaining odds and ends of household goods. One dull afternoon we finished mopping up the floors of the house, checked through the empty clothes closets and left the keys with the pickle man, who had given us a fine going-away party and gift the night before. Then we slowly rolled out of the driveway, the Chevvy lifting its two front wheels off the ground at the slightest bump, like a pup begging for a sandwich.

As we pulled away, the kids looked up from their enormous carton of toys, which took up about half the back seat, and started waving good-by to everything, until my wife and I joined in the game, calling out as we rolled away:

"Good-by, house!"

"Good-by, veranda!"

"Good-by, fence!"

"Good-by, driveway!"

"Good-by, Toronto!"

"Good-by!"

My younger daughter, Mary, was inclined to get carsick. We'd checked with our doctor, and he had prescribed some medicine, which we gave her just before setting out. He had told us that it might make her a bit dopey. He hadn't told us that she'd get corked. On the way to the cottage she sat in her little car seat getting higher and higher, grinning at us happily and waving her bottle, while we looked at each other in horror and began to watch in the rear-vision mirror for cops. By the time we arrived at the lake, in a late, wet spring snowstorm, she gave one last ecstatic chortle and passed out.

I managed to get a frantic call through to the doctor on a rural telephone. He was an imperturbable man with a low, slow voice. Actually he was a very fine doctor and a well-known child specialist. He told me that perhaps he'd prescribed too big a dose. He said just to leave her alone, and she'd sleep it off. She slept for eighteen hours, woke up without even a hangover, gave a great chuckle, and started running faster than ever, fascinated by the fact that the countryside had all turned white and convinced, I think, that she'd slept right through to the following Christmas.

We were now as free as birds. The only catch was that we were surrounded by snow, and most of the birds were still in Florida waiting for the North to warm up. All our friends were in the city, living like people. We were the only ones living among the trees and the boarded-up cottages and the squirrels.

When the snow melted, we lived more like otters. The roads around the cottage were still a foot deep in cold mud and ice water. There was one puddle in front of our cottage that I used to go through like a Coast Guard cutter, all the family hanging out the windows giving me soundings.

Our cottage was heated by a fireplace, something that's very picturesque but useless for anything but setting fire to the trees outside. We had ours blazing so hard that we threw shadows on the walls at high noon, and at night I heaped it with coal that I hauled from the village in the Chevvy. Nothing ever happened except within a foot of the fireplace, where it was so hot you couldn't stand it. The bedrooms remained the temperature of melting snow, and we always went to bed packed in hot-water bottles, until we found that we could heat the whole cottage easily with a little electric heater the landlord loaned us, along with the electric toaster and our electric hot plate. I can enjoy watching an oak log burning as well as anyone, but when it really gets cold, give me the sight of a glowing little electric wire.

I built a swing in the woods for the children, arranged my books, tools and typewriter and settled down to be a writer. I started getting up about six in the morning. I'd stack about two inches of copy paper beside me, twist a sheet into the typewriter, put my fingers on the keys, sit there listening to the sound of the world rotating on its axis and start falling asleep, my mind an absolute blank. I'd wake up, tell myself brusquely that the trouble was that I was sitting down to my typewriter before I had clearly organized in my *mind* what I wanted to say and wander out for a go at the kids' swing while I did some deep thinking. Nothing starts subconscious escape mechanisms operating like a pile of blank copy paper with no excuses for not filling it.

In short, it was my first experience at being my own boss, and with the psychological hazards of free-lance writing I probably would have gone mad if I'd been left to myself much longer. But soon the mud dried up, the chicory and buttercups grew waist high, and the summer cottagers began to appear, a bit surprised to find that someone had been there already for a month. I began to have visitors.

These were people I'd never met before who, as soon as they discovered I was a writer, began wondering what old junk they had lying around that they could carry over to

34

my cottage. They'd appear at my door saying, "Heard you were a writer—thought you might like to look these over," and hand me a pile of back copies of the *Rotarian, Popular Mechanics,* the *Ontario Motorist,* folders on the Bahamas, manuals on touch typing and the stories of paint companies. "Of course you mightn't get anything out of them," they'd say.

It was my first taste of the queer way people behave when you tell them you're a writer. Shy men in old, battered hats; brisk, nervous salesmen on holidays; illusive men who stood sideways to me when they talked, peering toward the bay, handed me bundles of stock market analyses, reprints from *Fortune* on the future of calculating machines and house organs full of breezy little notices about bridal showers and the employees who had broken their legs.

One morning, when I thought I'd been visited by everyone and that there was no more stuff left anywhere to be hauled over to my place, a big, friendly woman from Newfoundland, whose husband ran the boat-rental service, arrived at my door, wheezing horribly, with a whole carton of jigsaw puzzles. "Heard you were a writer," she panted.

She went on to say that she had a nephew who used to be a writer.

"One day I caught him chopping up a perfectly good piano out in the garage," she said. "When I saw what he was doing, I said, 'Land's sake, what in the world are you doing that for?' 'Oh, it's so old it doesn't work any more. I'm going to make a desk out of it,' he said. Well, by golly, he chopped it up and I didn't have a piano *or* a desk for years."

35

Having told me this, she disappeared into the woods and I've never seen her since. I couldn't get my mind on anything but her nephew for days.

That summer people also started sticking books in my hand as they were leaving my cottage or as I was leaving theirs. "Read that," they'd say.

I'd open my mouth to say that I already was behind on my sales market reports and house organs.

"Just read it, that's all," they'd say, nodding mysteriously.

If I implied politely that I didn't want to read about Australian aborigines right then, they'd snap, "Why not? They're very interesting. Wait till you read about some of the flutes they make."

People gave me thick paper-backed books that traced the lives of old Louisiana families through four generations and said, "I couldn't get through the first chapter. You read it."

But the summer visitors weren't any more fascinated with me than I was with them. I became absorbed in watching the changing shifts of people on their two weeks' vacations. I watched them arrive as pale as peeled potatoes, quickly turn a fiery red, shed their skins and, just as the new skin was turning brown, go home again. I watched them try to kill, drown and maim themselves. I watched them arrive after fifty weeks of cigarettes, banana splits and long winter months of sitting on their air-foam chair pads, do a beautiful crawl out into the lake, run out of wind, muscle and ideas, decide to walk back and sink like stones. I watched a small flotilla of people with their bottoms tucked in inner tubes, waving their hands languidly in the water like little propellers and floating out toward the horizon humming "Aloha Oe," without the faintest idea of how they were going to get back.

But the thing I found the most fascinating was the whole phenomenon of summer vacations with pay. I watched people who suddenly had nothing to do for two weeks but be happy stand around yawning and looking at trees and do all sorts of things to break up the boredom. I watched them change the positions of outhouses that were good for another five years; dig holes so deep that their wives could hardly hear them when they called up from the bottom to ask what time supper would be ready; move entire groves; tear down docks and build them up again and talk about moving the lake back two feet. It used to make me wonder what's going to happen when the work week has finally been reduced to zero and everybody is free to do exactly what he wants.

Another thing I wondered about was why husbands took their wives with them on holidays and vice versa. By the end of the summer I had a lot of firsthand information on the very controversial question of whether husbands and wives should take separate holidays. It's a subject about which there's a lot of confusion.

One day, when I'd driven into Toronto from the cottage, I was standing outside a restaurant checkroom when I met a talkative woman I'd known for years. She had a way of putting her hand on my arm, closing her eyes, saying, "So nice!" and backing away from me, without having the faintest idea of what either of us had said. This time, in the confusion, she must have said something about holidays and was my wife with me, because I remember mumbling that she was at a cottage.

37

She disappeared around a pillar, and a few minutes later I found myself standing behind her and her husband in a line-up for tables. She was still talking.

"They're going on separate holidays," she was saying. "I never *could* see how she could *stand* him, but I don't believe in *any* marriage breaking up."

After spending July and August watching married couples on holidays, I believed that every marriage, including this woman's, should break up regularly, for at least a couple of weeks a year. All the time she was talking, her husband, a vague, pear-shaped little man, stood with his hands in his pockets, peering over the tables as if at a distant island, spreading his pants out like a sail. I couldn't help thinking he was trying to catch a breeze someplace—someplace where nobody ever talks. His marriage should have broken up long enough for him to see if he could get there.

Few husbands and wives like the same kind of holiday. In the latter part of July I often ran into a man I'd known for years in Toronto—a delivery man for a dry-cleaning company. His idea of an idyllic interlude was to rent a cottage about ten feet square at the main part of our beach, where cottagers picked up their mail, coal oil and saddle horses and got away as quickly as possible. He would sit inside drinking beer with as many of his family and friends as he could get to visit him.

They sat around arguing about baseball and politics, all wearing suits, with vests and sometimes hats, and looking as if they'd just arrived from Minsk. They raised their voices above the thump of juke boxes, the clank of horseshoes, the clatter of a bowling alley. Horses galloped past .

38

the door, ridden by men in blue business suits and boys without shirts. The dust threw a sad brown light over the whole scene, including his wife, whose idea of a vacation was to lie flat on her back on a windy hill.

One woman who took a cottage near ours dragged her husband around every day visiting the sites of Indian settlements. I learned that she'd done this for years. She'd stand in the middle of these old sites and say, "Just think, hundreds of years ago people lived here," and drive to another site. Her husband would get so bored he'd begin to look like one of the Indians dug up again. He would have liked to have spent his holidays in some little shack, quietly going to seed.

One good reason for a husband and his wife to take separate holidays is that it gives them a better appreciation of each other and marriage in general. One good friend of mine, a specialty-food salesman who spent his week ends near us at the beach, became so obsessed with getting away from his wife for a holiday that the idea practically became a hobby of his.

"I'd just like to do what I want—*when* I want," he'd say. "I mean if I wanted to lie down and read, say, something about the early Romans at four in the afternoon, and I got so interested in it that I didn't want to stop for supper, well, I wouldn't *have* to stop."

He talked about it so much that he began to fascinate his wife, who had often secretly wondered what it would be like to have something tall and continental chase her around a fountain.

"Of course, as it said in an article I read the other day," this man said to me one week end, his eyes aglow, " 'Taking

39

separate holidays is packed with dynamite. A man may have so many affairs that he will return to his marriage emotionally exhausted.' "

It was obvious that he was in real need of giving it a try: he'd stepped right through the looking glass. Having so many summer romances that you're exhausted may happen to people who look like young movie stars, but most people, who are built in the shapes of various roots, won't be bothered by anything but squirrels. The chance of anything really demoralizing happening in two weeks is about as probable as winning a trip around the world for a box top.

But this man and his wife decided to give separate holidays a try. The first two weeks in August they both came to the beach, where they'd been coming for years, but this time he went to their own cottage, and she rented a friend's place on a point opposite across the bay. They each solemnly agreed to pretend the other wasn't there.

He took along Plutarch's *Lives,* which he had been putting off for years but couldn't put off any longer, as well as two self-help books called *Personality With Power Steering* and *The Well-Adjusted Administrator,* but forgot to take along a change of socks, underwear, his glasses and the keys to the cottage. He had to break the lock and spent one day repairing it and the second being sick from some toadstools he cooked. On the third he met a fascinating little blond divorcee who went for a ride with him in his outboard and later, helping him to land his gear, dropped his motor into ten feet of water. He spent the next day salvaging it, and the next he dropped in on his wife.

She, in the meantime, had struck up a friendship with a tall, cultured Englishman, who had finally taken her to a

40

party. After several drinks of lemonade into which he poured something that he said jovially would put purple pants on it, pouring quite a bit more into his own, he drove her home. He saw her to her cottage, asked her frigidly who she was and why she was following him, bowed from the waist and did a half gainer over a veranda railing. Since then she had spent her evenings reading some old magazines she had found behind a pile of kindling.

But from the time her husband called on her, the prospect brightened. Each became absorbed in how the other was making out. Her husband would go over and peek in her window, come back and say to me, "Well, she's at the jigsaw again," or "had poached eggs for supper tonight. Did them a bit too soft for me, though." She used to get a friend to report on whether he was sending his laundry out or doing it himself.

They had a wonderful time. It was more fun than bird watching. Sometimes they'd stand on their porches waving to each other across the bay and looking a bit like an illustration for a calendar. Finally they moved in with each other again and didn't talk any more about separate holidays.

It would have been a good idea if a lot of the people I saw on vacation that summer had tried the same thing. Holidays may, as some experts claim, be the only time of year most married couples can really be together twenty-four hours a day. But I've noticed that, in terms of the average holiday at a summer resort, the woman doesn't get any more chance to see her husband than she does at home. What happens is that her husband looks around fondly at the pump, the wood stove and the holes gnawed by deer mice and chortles: "This is what I like! A real *change!*"

41

But the only change for his wife is that she prepares the same meals as she does at home on equipment from a museum of pioneer implements and crockery. She also cooks for half a dozen extra people who arrive from the city on week ends, hand her a roast, a ham, a chicken and some vegetables and sink into lawn chairs, figuring they've done their share. They provided the food; all she has to do is cook it.

My wife, in fact, was the first one on the beach to see the point of this. At the same time she realized that she was in a better position than any of the other women to correct it, as this wasn't a two-week holiday for us, but an embarkation on a new and permanent way of life which she didn't intend to let get off on the wrong foot. I was living at home all day, every day, month on end, and already I was watching her dampen clothes, tie pigtails, make beds and make stew. I was beginning my career as probably the hottest male authority on housework on the continent. I'd put my thoughts up in curlers and had begun sticking my nose into my wife's work, and it reached a point where she figured that if I was going to retire on the profits from the house, there was no reason why she shouldn't have a real ball herself. So she decided to let me look after the family for a week while she visited a girl friend in Kitchener.

I'd developed a theory that if men were to make a time-and-motion study of housework the way they do in industry, they could cut down a lot of waste effort. "Trouble with you," I'd often say to my wife, looking at her dreamily over my tpewriter, "you're not organized."

The next week I discovered that there's more to housework than being organized. It's also important to be a woman. A woman has an instinct for housekeeping that was already operating when she was a little girl dressing dolls, playing house and watching her mother cook. A man trying to catch on to the knack of housekeeping in a week is like a woman suddenly deciding to overhaul a car.

What caused me the most trouble was cooking. My wife can start around four in the afternoon getting something ready to simmer, stew or brown for supper. From then on she can put things on to bake, boil or fry at irregular intervals and at six o'clock can announce calmly that supper is ready and have it all come out even. Whenever I tried to cook more than two things for the same meal, the whole thing ended like a dog race.

I'd start lunch for myself and the kids, putting a couple of pieces of bread in the toaster (an old-style, manually operated one that someone had saved for the cottage) and starting to heat some beans. I'd open a can of soup, empty it into a saucepan, get out the milk and remember that I hadn't started my coffee. I'd put the milk down, put the coffee on, drop a few eggs into the frying pan and remember the soup, smell the toast burning, come back to the eggs and notice that the beans were boiling.

When finally everything would be sizzling, perking, toasting and burning, I'd be making little stabbing motions like somebody trying to put out a grass fire. I'd shake the beans, blow on my fingers, flip the toaster, baste the eggs, turn the bacon and shake the soup, shake the coffee percolator, shake the kids, yell for help and turn everything off. We'd sit down to eat everything just the way it was. It would either have a thin skin over it or be raw inside. Mary would take one mouthful and say, "I hope Mummy isn't dead."

43

I managed to get some washing done that week, but not if I washed dishes too. By the middle of the week I was losing ground fast. I hadn't been able to wash a dish for three days, and I was serving the kids their milk in Martini glasses. My wife had told me once that the reason I always got into such messes in the kitchen was that I didn't put things away as I used them. If I'd stopped to put everything away as I used it, I'd have missed the main things—meals.

I managed to braid the kids' hair, often by getting the one I was working on to lie down flat on her face while I straddled her so that she couldn't move and sticking down stray bits with vaseline.

Ordering the right amounts of food was something else that bothered me. Even ordering a thing like the right amount of bread requires a special sense developed only over a period of years. We had bread delivery, and when the breadman asked me if I needed any, I'd stand there imagining myself eating bread, Mary eating bread and Jane eating bread and try to add it up. I would feel each of us eating, say, about five slices. Then I'd have to estimate how many times five slices would go into a loaf.

In the meantime the breadman would be looking at me as if he were thinking, "This guy doesn't even make a good housewife." Inside the house other things would be burning, boiling over, getting dirtier and crying. I'd make a snap decision and order too much. I threw out so much bread in a week that every time I opened the door, so many birds and chipmunks would take off that it looked like Disneyland.

I made one try at putting one of my ingenious systems to work. I decided I'd do the ironing bit by bit, whenever I had a free moment. It started as a system and ended as a grim running fight against increasing odds, ironing things not when I had a free moment, but as they were needed. I dragged the ironing board around with me like a crown-and-anchor game, setting it up wherever I could find a space that was clear, fishing a slip or a dress out of an old, long, flat carton I kept behind the refrigerator, getting the mildew off it the best I could and trying to iron it before something burned.

My wife was coming back on Saturday, and on Friday the final breakdown came. I began to understand why wives occasionally sit down and cry, and I probably would have tried it myself if I hadn't been afraid the breadman would catch me. So I just sat down and took stock of what had to be done in twenty-four hours. No beds were made. For the first few days I'd made them each morning, but I'd decided that, compared with the basic battle for food and clothing, they were unimportant and had started just pulling the spread up over them each morning. Crawling into bed at night had begun to feel like getting into a sandy bathing suit. I would have to tidy things up just to be able to walk around. Most of the ironing was still to be done. The stuff I'd managed to get through was stacked on top of the icebox, and dirty dishes were stacked wherever I could find a ledge.

I decided I had to get the kids out for the day, feed them something ready-made from the store, abandon all my theories and just keep working until I could see daylight, which, as a matter of fact, I did. I finished the ironing at four in the morning, met my wife at eight-thirty, slept for fifteen hours and from then on found it a lot easier to make myself stay at my typewriter.

ALL that summer we prepared for our safari south. We bought an electric hot plate and a little alcohol stove and planned to pack a teapot, dishes and silverware, so that we could make ourselves snacks for next to nothing in motor courts and at the side of the road. We bought a steamer trunk, a rubber ground sheet, a big flashlight and a concertina-type luggage carrier to clamp to the running board of the car. We sent away for strip maps from Toronto to Miami to Los Angeles and took an overnight test hop in the Chevvy to North Bay. Mary was sick all over everything, and we had a flat tire and threw a fan belt, but for some reason that I can't explain now we didn't get discouraged. We still planned to migrate with the birds in September.

But one difference between us and the birds was that we had to migrate via the United States Consulate in Toronto. I popped down to Toronto one morning to get the whole thing cleared up. Three weeks later I trudged up the Consulate steps again, moving my lips silently as I checked off the things I'd been told to get and carrying in an envelope two copies of my police clearance, two certified copies of my birth certificate, three identical passport photographs, an unexpired passport, a signed statement in duplicate listing the value of all my assets and resources, the results of V.D. tests, X rays of my family's chests and a statement from my bank. All of these, along with miscellaneous documentary corroboration, made a file about two inches thick.

This was when I made my first acquaintance with a dark, pleasant young officer in the Consulate whom I got to know well by sight before September and for whom I developed a strange attachment. He used to answer questions at the counter for everyone but me. I was always out of turn, no matter what turn I came in. I don't mean that he was rude. He never once gave the impression of being anything but efficiently courteous. In fact, I got the feeling that he

47

rather liked to see my family and me and didn't want us to leave too soon. Every time I'd come up to the counter and say "I—uh—" he'd motion politely with his pencil to the benches and say, "Just sit down, please."

I'd go back and sit down. Ten more guys would come in, go up to the counter and be handed cards. I'd figure, well, now the dam's broke. Everybody's going up to the counter. The system has broken down. I'd join the line. He'd never look up. I don't know how he'd know I was there. He must have developed a sort of radar for me. But as soon as I reached him and said, "I—uh—" he'd motion with his pencil without looking up and say, "Just sit down, please."

I'd finally give up and disappear into the crowd, convinced that you needed some special influence or something to get to talk to anyone but determined to sit there until they swept me out with a broom. I'd become vaguely aware that people were looking at me. I'd look toward the counter. The young man would point his pencil at me and motion me up to the head of a line of about twenty-five people with the same expression of courtly detachment.

I was finally given an appointment. As anyone knows who has obtained a visa, this appointment is the climax of many weeks of asking questions about what you should do now and scurrying around for material and being told all sorts of gruesome stories about people who sat on a hard bench for thirty-six hours without eating, waiting to be called, and it's loaded with suspense. You appear at the Consulate at the time set for you and wait your call, the same as you do when you're getting your driver's license. But instead of waiting for each person ahead of you to go through some simple process like filling out a license card, it's like waiting for each person to buy a house or make an ocean crossing. Missing your turn would be like forgetting to attend your own wedding.

Our appointment was for nine o'clock. We'd waited six weeks for it. We got there at eight-thirty. At eight-forty-five we stood before a pair of closed doors, the first in a long line. We took turns holding Mary. At eight-fifty-nine, we heard rustling sounds behind the doors. At eight-fifty-nine-and-a-half, the doors opened. I headed the parade to the counter, holding Mary. The dark young man was sitting there on a high stool, freshly shaved and looking fit for some fun with me. I shifted Mary to my other arm, held up my envelope full of papers, said, "I—uh—," and the dark young man motioned with his pencil and said, "Just sit down, please."

We sat on the front bench, all in a row, where nobody could overlook us. The young man picked up a card, looked at it, looked at us obviously ready to start the appointments. We moved forward on our bench, ready to move up fast when we were called, and Mary said, "I have to go to the bathroom."

My wife and I turned pale. All around us were pink granite walls and men in uniform. I'd never been in a place where I'd consider it less likely to find a bathroom.

What made the situation more fantastic was that we knew Mary wasn't serious. She was just bored. We tried to ignore her, but she repeated the statement in flat, decided tones. We soothed her and explained that we would miss our appointment, and how would she like that? We asked her hysterically how she'd like to hear the story of

49

The Poky Little Puppy. We tried explaining to her that people just don't go to the bathroom in the American Consulate. It's a pretty hard story to make convincing.

It took a lot of explaining to make the people at the Consulate understand why we weren't there when we were called. I don't think anyone was ever quite convinced except perhaps the young man on the stool. Somehow I always felt that he believed me and was having a hard time hiding a sense of amused triumph at having finally made me crack.

I went through a grilling. Where are you going? To the United States. What *part* of the United States? Well, just any old part, you see—— What is your destination? Uh, well, Miami. What is your address there? Pardon? Your address in Miami. Oh, well, general delivery. Do you intend to overthrow the United States Government? No. Have you any contagious disease? No. Is there any insanity in your family?

By this time I was beginning to wonder. But it was too late. I was fingerprinted, thumbprinted, blueprinted, filed away for future reference, listed, categorized, given a number and a lecture, called a resident alien and a potential immigrant and stared at with my pants down by a doctor. Finally we were all herded into an office where a kindly, quiet man with gray hair teased the kids, told me he'd always wanted to write himself, shook hands with us, welcomed us to the United States of America, wished us luck and gave us our visas.

There was one other thing to do before starting on our trip. We planned to cover a lot of country in the car in the next few months, and I decided that my wife should know how to drive. Every now and then, ever since we'd had the car, I had taken a crack at teaching her, but usually we'd be back in about half an hour, my wife sobbing, my daughters hugging her, and me saying, "Okay, okay. I'm sorry I used that word. But, after all, a clutch costs about sixteen bucks."

Now I decided to change all that. I made up my mind to have another go at it and to be calm and reasonable no matter what happened.

These days, with more and more people driving cars in their teens, with instruction in driving included with high-school education, and with cars becoming easier and easier to drive, the day seems about here when women won't have to "learn" how to drive any more than men. They'll just "know," the same as they know how to use a telephone. I hope so, because, although there are schools that teach women how to drive and schools that teach men how to drive, there are no schools that teach men how to teach women how to drive.

The first few lessons in this superschool should provide a sort of specialized public-speaking course to teach a man to keep his mind on what he's saying no matter what his wife is doing to the car. Then, when his wife grips the wheel as if she had hold of the cleaner who shrunk her dress, flushes a deep pink and starts out of the driveway like a spawning salmon, yelling, "How-can-I-watch-where-I'm-going-with-all-those-other-things-you-told-me to-do?" he'd simply say in a calm, reassuring monotone, "The motor is going much too fast, dear, and you are moving the clutch in and out." Instead of which he grabs his glasses and says something like: "Holy—! I could drive this car out of this driveway with my head upside down!"

When my wife got behind the wheel, I'd find myself

shouting utter nonsense—I don't know why. It was just that things immediately became crazily confused. I'd yell that cars coast uphill, that only streetcars stop for red lights and that airplanes don't need horns. One time I found myself trying to prove that onions don't smell.

You'd hardly believe it, I know, but it's the kind of thing a man finds himself saying when his nerves begin to go. We'd just started the gear-changing lesson and I'd said, "If you just get the picture of the letter 'H.' "

"Now don't start shrieking at me," my wife said.

"But look, all I said was the gearshift is——"

"It's the *way* you said it," my wife said. "Sitting there smirking in that superior way of yours. After all, you didn't invent the automobile."

I said, "Look, why don't we just forget all this? I'll do all the driving."

"And what am I supposed to do all my life?" my wife snapped through her tears. "Just sit around the kitchen all day smelling of onions?"

"For Pete's sake, I never said you smell like onions," I said.

"Oh, so now onions don't smell?"

"ALL ONIONS DON'T SMELL," I yelled, baring my teeth.

That night I heard my wife tell a girl friend, "Honestly, I thought he'd go insane. All he did was sit there screaming, 'Onions don't smell.' "

Another feature of the course on how to teach driving to a woman would be a brief course on driving for men. This would not be to teach men how to drive, but to make sure they don't forget how to drive. It's easier to forget than most men think. Before I started to teach my wife how to drive, I operated a car as unconsciously as I'd lift a glass of beer. Before the third lesson I'd become so conscious of how far to shove a clutch in or when to change gears that I had some sort of psycho-physical breakdown. From the first time I caught my wife with her head near the floor watching what I did with the clutch, I tried to let the clutch out better than anyone had ever done since the car was invented. I'd make the car jump. My wife would straighten up with a sphinxlike smile.

"Okay," I'd yelp. "Five million guys do that at least once a day."

"You did exactly what I did when you used that language last Sunday."

"DID I RUN INTO A FENCE?"

"It wasn't a fence. It was a tree."

One time I grabbed a flashlight that was lying on the seat and said, "If I hit myself over the head with this, do you haveta hit yourself over the head with it?" I heard a woman who was sitting on her screened porch across the road call to her husband, "George! He's going to strike that poor girl. Stop him!"

When George wandered sheepishly down to the road to see if there was any truth in it, we got talking. He told me out of the corner of his mouth that the last time he gave his wife a driving lesson, she ran crossways over a celery farm.

My school of driving would also include several lessons under some such heading as: "An Introduction to a Study of Modern Woman in Relation to the Internal Combustion Engine." Not that it's necessary to understand an automobile engine in order to drive a car, but it's a good idea. It's even interesting. Some husbands make the mistake of thinking that their wives will find it interesting too. Nothing could be farther from the truth. My wife is as interested in the principle of the gasoline engine as I am in learning how to smock.

I remember the first time I tried to explain things. I sat down with her at the kitchen table, lit a cigarette and said: "You see, the gasoline is mixed with air to make a combustible vapor, then it's drawn into the cylinder and fired by a spark, and the explosion drives the piston and turns a crankshaft."

My wife looked at me, yawned and said: "Don't you think it's time you got a haircut? You look like Mortimer Snerd."

A woman doesn't really want to learn how to drive. She only wants to make use of the most rapid method devised so far for picking up seam binding, celery hearts and spools of number forty thread. About what goes on between calls, she couldn't care less.

Every now and then, when I'd think my wife had a pretty clear picture of how a car operates, she would ask me something like, "Is there enough gas in the battery?"

I'd groan and say, "Look, you got any idea what makes a car go?"

"The spark plugs, of course."

I'd try to be patient. "The spark plugs just explode the gas in the cylinders. What are the cylinders? What drives the wheels around and makes the car go along the highway?"

"The things that work the starter."

I'd hold my head. "How do they do that?"

"They make the spark go 'round."

"What do you think I meant the other day by all that stuff about connecting rods and the crankshaft?"

"Crankshaft? You told me yourself that cars don't have cranks any more!"

The irony of it is that even with this sort of knowledge a woman can still make a man look as if he doesn't know a gearshift from a glove compartment. I began piloting my wife into the bustling near-by town where we did our shopping. My wife would approach an intersection, spring at a melee of transports, baby carriages, old men and traffic cops like a starving lion after a hartebeest. If I'd moderately suggest caution, she would whip around at me and say, "How can I make the car go slow when I have all those things to do?" Perhaps she'd add, "How can I drive a car when the horn doesn't work?"

One time I yelled, "I could drive a car for fifteen years without a horn." I immediately found myself in a position where I either used the horn or drove into a hydrant with a cop standing beside it.

The last and most important phase of the course at my special school would be a study of feminine psychology. Just because a woman is in a car doesn't mean that she has stopped being a woman. Nothing changes a woman, not even sitting behind six exploding cylinders. When a man says something like, "I told you yesterday what a carburetor is, and it's not the thing you pour oil into," it sets up tremendous emotional vibrations. Two men can discuss a car without emotion. But a woman goes at a driving lesson the way she'd go to the wedding of a favorite niece.

Every definition that I gave of the car my wife regarded as a slur on her character. The first time I referred to the rear end, she pulled up to the curb, yanked on the brake, folded her arms and said: "I *won't* be sworn at."

I was probably one of the last guys to teach his wife to drive. It's a good thing. I can imagine trying to teach my wife to drive some of the products of today's automotive industry. I have visions of myself sitting out on a country road yelling, "I told you yesterday that you don't touch the super-hydraulic, self-energizing, hydro-cooled vapor release until you've let out the !'*%$#"! cushion-flow, automatic, chemically sealed, triple-action speed selector."

I take no credit for it whatever, but my wife did become a very competent driver, and by the time we nosed the Chevvy south that September she was ready to spell me at the wheel.

THE other cottagers left after Labor Day week end, and we had the resort almost to ourselves. The leaves had turned. The goldenrod, wild mustard, plantain, burdock and chickory were waist deep. The days were warm and mellow, the mornings so frosty we had to light the wood stove. It was beautiful. I didn't get any work done, but it was beautiful.

And one golden, hazy day we started south after the last robin. As we pulled away we all waved and called:

"Good-by, cottage!"

"Good-by, lake!"

"Good-by, dock!"

The Chevvy, minus the trailer but loaded to the dome light, started its last trip over the washboard road to the highway, purring like a sewing machine. There was luggage lashed to everything outside and almost as much inside, including a complete play pen and a full supply of toys.

In the late afternoon we crossed the International Bridge at Niagara Falls and rolled into the United States Customs and Immigration like a secondhand luggage store on wheels. My kids had all their dolls sitting in a row across the back seat, and the United States immigration inspector, after asking my wife and me where we were born, continued with the kids, and, with dead-pan seriousness, right through all the dolls. The kids spoke up for each doll, with utter fascination. The customs inspector took one look at my lashings of luggage and waved us on, and we rolled into the United States singing, "O say, can you see, by the dawn's early light." We stopped early at some cabins, and I puzzled my way through about sixty feet of knotted clothesline to get at our luggage as it started to rain. That night I went into a little all-night diner and, over a cup of coffee, figured out a diagram of how to tie and untie the luggage to the car and kept it in the glove compartment from then on.

It was pouring rain the next morning. Although I never believe these things when other people tell them, they're so obviously phony and hackneyed, the roof of the Chevvy leaked. My only explanation is that this Chevvy had very hackneyed ideas. We drove about twenty-five miles in the wrong direction and found ourselves in a historical park, peering through the downpour at plaques we didn't particularly want to see.

It took us four days to get to New York. (Did I say that we thought we might as well see New York too while we were at it?) It was a distance of about five hundred miles and a fight all the way. When the sun went down, my lights went out. At least they seemed to. They couldn't hold their own with anything more powerful than a bed lamp, and if there was much traffic coming against me, I lost sight of the shoulder of the highway at sundown and didn't see it again till next morning. After a few hours of this kind of night driving and watching for a motor court, anything with a roof looked good, and a few times that was about all we got. Our last stop was in a squalid little nest of cabins just outside of New York. Here we first tried out our electric hot plate. The only wall plug in the cabin was in the bathroom. We made our toast on top of the toilet seat, which my wife, always the perfect housekeeper, covered daintily with a tablecloth.

But it was worth it, as for me a trip to New York has always been. At that time it was almost impossible to get a room in New York without reservations, but we managed to get one room, with one bed, for the four of us. We all slept on it crosswise, my wife and I with our feet on an inverted dresser drawer that we'd placed on two chairs alongside the bed. It's evidently a very healthful way to sleep, because I got up at five in the morning feeling so good I walked from our hotel in the Seventies to the Battery and back before breakfast with the family.

We left New York in the afternoon. We drove through the Holland Tunnel with a convoy of trucks, roared out onto the Pulaski Skyway, neck and neck with trucks that could have taken the Chevvy on their tailgates, took the wrong turn and raced back for the Holland Tunnel again with a new batch of trucks going the other way and not a chance of getting off as far as I could see till I got back to Canada. I did manage to peel out of formation, though. I parked and got through the traffic on foot to ask directions from a workman I'd seen at the side of the road. He showed me how to get turned around.

From then on I managed to keep pointed the right way, at least most of the time. My wife acted as map reader and navigator and did an uncannily good job of it. It was uncanny because she did it with some other brain process than the ones men use. There's more to the belief that women operate by intuition than we generally suspect. A man is uncomfortable unless he hears the fine precision-tooled gears of logic meshing behind all his actions. If a woman ever becomes involved with logic at all, she treats it the way my wife treated angles, directions and geometric axioms in general—with a sort of friendly disbelief. Somewhere under her finger wave parallel lines met and crossed one another, and light rays had been bent long before Einstein. She referred to the directions east, west, across, along and around as loosely as she talked about gears and spark plugs. Yet by some process like the migratory instinct of birds, she always arrived where she wanted to go without knowing where she'd been, while I always knew where I was going with logical clarity but ended up with my radiator against brick walls or in people's private driveways.

"You'll turn south on Main Street if you want to stop for a typewriter ribbon," she'd say in some strange town, putting down her map and nodding toward the north.

"You mean I go *north* on Main Street for a typewriter ribbon."

"That's right. You'd never find a typewriter ribbon here on the highway."

"I'm not talking about shopping facilities. I'm talking about the points of the compass."

"Well . . ." My wife would glance around. "We're going east," she'd say.

I'd peer at her sideways, as if I'd just seen a distant sail.

"Oh—all right." She'd flush and glance at me, her eyes bright with something besides adoration. "Let's see. Where's the sun?" She'd peer down some street.

"Look," I'd say patiently. "The sun rises in the east and sets in the west."

One time when I said this, she said, "Aren't you clever. After all, Columbus discovered that five hundred years ago."

I was always trying to equate what went on in my wife's head to my fourth-form geometry, and I usually found myself with a lot of loose angles left over. Not only that, it usually left *me* facing the wrong way.

Once it left me in another country altogether. We were parked beside the highway having some hamburgs when a woman of about fifty in red pants and a white gob hat came

61

over to our car and asked the way to a little town we'd driven through and which had reminded me, for some reason, of a place I used to visit as a kid.

My wife told her. "You go south," she said, pointing east, "to a bridge, then go that other way and just keep on to where the other motor court is."

The other woman seemed to understand this. She said, "You mean you go around until you're at that fork where it's all lumpy?"

"That's right—" my wife smiled—"but you don't pass the gas station. You turn straight ahead."

I couldn't stand it any longer. "You go east to Highway 22A," I snapped. "You cross two bridges."

My wife looked at me quickly. "You mean one bridge," she said.

"You cross two bridges," I said, in perfect control of myself, ignoring my wife.

"But we've only crossed one bridge since we stopped for gas," my wife said.

I pursed my lips and studied a near-by tree like Charles Laughton looking up at a yardarm. "There are two," I said, "but if you think there's only one, it's up to you," I said, clearly picturing the two bridges.

I smiled at the woman again, just as I remembered that the other bridge I'd been thinking of was at Wasaga Beach in Canada.

When I tried to straighten things out the best I could, the woman in the red pants started to nod her head slowly about two inches from my face. "Ya-ya-ya-ya-ya," she said. "Just like my husband. He knows everything."

My wife and she had a good talk after that about the price of play shoes.

62

Women band together in this sort of thing. Another time my wife stood on top of a monument, looked south and said, "I can see the Laurentians."

"You looking in a mirror or something?" I yodeled.

A stout woman with dark glasses looked over at her and said, "How they hate to be told anything, don't they?" She nodded toward her husband, a stout man who was standing off by himself looking the right way. "He's just the same. Stubborn as an ox."

I was thinking of a few experiences like this while driving around Washington when I got into a traffic snarl. Washington is one of those cities which are built like a wheel, and I soon found myself going 'round and 'round, making a complete orbit about every ten minutes. My wife kept telling me to turn east, pointing west. I kept so busy trying to get her straightened out by pointing out the shadows cast by the sun that I passed the same cop three times, each time going the wrong way on a different one-way street.

The first time, he held up traffic and got me turned around.

"Now we're going right," my wife gloated. "South."

We were going north. I swore, circled around till I was going the opposite way on the next street down. The cop, in the meantime, had strolled down a block. I passed him again, smiling sheepishly, going the wrong way. He watched me curiously but didn't stop me, evidently figuring that it was all part of the first mistake and that it would be better to let me work it out myself, and strolled down another block, where I passed him again, going the wrong way.

This time he stopped me, leaned on my window and said, "Look, Buddy. Suppose you tell me where you want to go and we'll see if we can work something out together."

I told him I wanted to go to Florida. He showed me, pointing out the route with his finger and tending to get his forehead closer and closer to mine and to jab more and more vigorously with his finger, until he'd check himself and, with a slight effort, resume his manner of official detachment.

I didn't make any more wrong turns, because I didn't stop to do any more sightseeing until we found ourselves in the South, which, to a northerner seeing it for the first time, is an exciting and pleasurable experience. My wife and I began to exchange pleased glances and remarks like "This is the climate for me!" Every time we stopped for gas or something to eat, we asked about the climate. When we were told by the filling-station attendant or waitress that they hardly ever got any snow, we knew that we were definitely getting nearer to the perfect place to live. We bowled along happily, pointing out cotton, mules, Negro shacks, white trash, Spanish moss, peanuts, buzzards, mocking birds and red mud. We wondered why more people didn't leave home.

We saw the Fountain of Youth in St. Augustine, where a girl in a Spanish costume gave us a drink of water which she guaranteed would make us ten years younger, and we all stood around watching the kids to see if they'd disappear. We went to Marineland. We looked through glass portholes at sting rays, moray eels, tortoises, sharks, and, in one of the smaller tanks, set into the wall like a jeweller's display, an octopus that must make atheists of a lot of viewers. We asked the attendant, as hundreds of people do daily, why the shark in the big tank didn't eat the other

64

fish and were told that he wasn't hungry, something nobody ever thinks of.

We kept on down the coast, lifting our faces happily to the warm sunshine and ocean breezes and feeling sorry for all the poor Canadians faced with six months of winter. But when we struck Daytona Beach we found that most of them were there ahead of us.

In 1763 England got Florida and Canada in exchange for Havana and a few West Indies islets in a deal she put through with a big stick. She kept Canada, but Florida got dealt off to Spain and finally ended up in the United States. Every winter approximately one hundred thousand shivering Canadians go down to see who got hold of the right end of the stick.

There are so many cars with Ontario licenses parked along Beach Street that Canadians who at first stop to talk to the folks from back home soon begin walking past one another with the same expression they wear in Toronto or Winnipeg. Newsstands display Canadian papers along with those of key American cities. The emblem displayed by some motor courts is the maple leaf. One operator said he just kept reading the Canadian papers and, as soon as the first big blizzard hit, ran up the Union Jack. The State Advertising Commission of Florida received eight thousand responses from Canada to one direct-mail campaign. One Ontario man lobbied to get the Canadian government to drop pensions to veterans and, instead, buy them farms and homes in Florida.

In the meantime, the Floridians happily show Canadians alligators, snakes, cypress knees, swamps, porpoises, turtles, coconuts and conch shells. They offer them all the orange juice they can drink for ten cents (up to two cups), try to make up their minds whether they're Englishmen or Yankees and play safe by saying, "Y'all come back, now."

But at this point we were worried less about coming back than getting there, as we still hadn't found the place where we were going to stop, and we had reached that point of the motor trip where we were getting a bit glassy-eyed. We still had in our minds some picturesque little salt-bleached shack were a family as free of commitments as ours could live just as it chose and score a good one on the rich people. All we had to do was find it.

We began working our way down the coast, poking across the causeways to the beaches, getting quoted prices that made our new sun tans go blotchy, going farther south, turning across more causeways to more beaches, finding that the rates were gaining on us and finally coming to West Palm Beach. I thought I'd take one more try at finding our little shack on the shore. I turned across the causeway to Palm Beach and drove past a couple of miles of royal palms and nearly through the front door of Tiffany's before I gave up and headed back where I belonged, with the scrub, swamps and alligators. On the way, just for the hell of it, I priced one place, was quoted thirty-eight dollars a day and got bowed out between tall sun-tanned blondes by a European desk clerk, both of us ankle-deep in broadloom. When I was out on the street, I asked a cop where the poor man's Palm Beach was. He shoved his cap back, thought a minute and said, "Man, there ain't any!"

I headed back north with the whole family crying, including me. We gave up the idea of living in a little shack on the shore and just started looking for a little shack anywhere. We went back up Highway 1, this time turning left at each town, toward the jungle instead of the ocean.

Florida is still, to me, one of the most charming states in the Union, and I harbor a deep fondness for the whole Southland and its people. But if there's anything depressing, it's trying to beat the going prices in any community. I'll never forget some of the accommodations we looked at on this bargain hunt: little house trailers on cement blocks behind wheel-alignment shops and hamburg stands; old boxcars fixed up for a family of four; abandoned stills. Somebody would tell us he had this little place that just might do for us: funny, he'd say, he hadn't thought of it when we first started to speak. Nothing grand, understand, but it just might fill the bill. He'd get in his car and tell us to follow in ours. We'd drive along after him, getting sadder and sadder as we put more and more miles between us and the ocean, the beach, the highway, the stores, motels, people and the police force. Finally we'd arrive at the little place, sitting there among the Georgia pine, just the way it had been left after the last lynching.

One place we were shown was a former naval barracks. I remember looking down a dark corridor with a door at the far end making a rectangle of bright sunlight about the size of a postage stamp. It was like a cover illustration for a book in which the main character goes crazy. We looked at bathrooms as cozy as death chambers, with walls, floor and ceilings of unplastered, unpainted concrete. The proprietor would pull a string on a naked bulb hanging from the ceiling, dimly revealing a shower and a mirror. I'd look at my reflection in the semi-gloom, feeling like Edmund Dante.

We'd now been twelve days on the road, and the inside of the car looked like a cross between a broom closet and a Murphy bed in which four people had eaten several dozen hamburgers, ice-cream cones, chocolate bars and hot dogs, two of them while doing cutouts. Opening the door in a crowd was positively indecent. It was so bad that when I got out of the car, I looked up and down the street first, then opened the door as little as possible, sneaked out and shut it quickly again. At that, a couple of Coke bottles would usually slither out and bounce across the sidewalk after me. The way I looked after twelve days on the road in the same clothes, empty bottles bouncing out of a car after me didn't seem out of place.

We were circling around like buzzards, taking the odd lateral excursion inland, when our car (heh heh) broke down. It did it with a wonderful sense of low comedy in the middle of a swamp, with burlesque effects of smoke, fire, jerks and explosions under the hood. Come to think of it, considering that the roof leaked too, this was about the corniest car I've ever had.

Actually, my wife and Jane were asleep in the back seat, and Mary was asleep in the front, with her head on my lap under the steering wheel. It was a warm, drowsy southern afternoon. Everything was serene and peaceful inside and outside the car. There was hardly any traffic on the high-way, and very little of anything else, except a few dead pos-sums, and in spite of our problems, I was having a peaceful reverie at the wheel thinking that anyway I didn't have to cope with snow.

Our speedometer didn't work, but I figured I was doing about fifty-five, although I've often wondered since whether we really did go that fast in the old car or whether it just felt as if we were going that fast. I heard a soft *b-r-r-r* in the motor, like distant machine-gun fire. I eased up on the gas. The noise was still there. I pressed down on the gas again, and the noise stopped. I remember that I got a picture in my mind of something loose, and, in one of the maddest decisions of my life, decided that as long as I kept the motor pulling forward it would take up the slack till I got to the next town and found out what it was. I gave her the gun. There was a lurch and a crash. My wife sat up and yelled, "My God, save the children!" I came to a banging, horrible stop. We all got out of the car. Smoke was coming from under the hood. Hot oil was pouring across the highway into the ditch. I opened the hood. Two connecting rods were sticking out of the block like ears of corn. There was a hole in the block big enough for me to put my head in.

There was nothing in either direction along the highway but swamp and scrub. I stood there looking in a temporary trance, at the stream of oil. I heard wheels on the shoulder of the highway and could hardly believe my eyes when I looked up and saw a tow truck parked behind us. The driver, a thin, brown, grinning young man, was drunk. He said he was just out for a ride in his truck and waved aside any mention of money. He didn't want any. He said he'd be glad to tow us anywhere.

"Ah'll tow you around the world," he said happily.

He towed us to some little tourist cabins in the scrub a couple of miles along the highway. There was a lunch stand across the road from them. We unloaded all the luggage, I got the family into one of the cabins, and the tow-truck man and I took the Chevvy into a village about eight miles away.

We pulled into a brand-new garage that had just been opened by a semi-retired insurance salesman who had moved to Florida from South Carolina. He was a jolly southerner with an old-plantation accent and was still ambushing Yankees. He'd evidently figured he'd catch the greatest number if he pretended he could fix cars.

He told me, "Look yah. Ah'll fix yo' up a new motah. Ah'll get the best pahts from anothuh old motah, and take the best pahts from yo' motah, and build yo' a brand new motah." He gave me an inspiring talk on how he'd precision-tool the cylinder walls and the bearings, making it all sound as scientific as a brain operation, which was what I really needed.

By this time our morale had thrown a few connecting rods too. The place we'd stopped at had a kitchen attached, and we tried to boost our spirits by making ourselves a home-cooked meal. During supper I looked up and saw a cockroach running up the ice box. I got up casually, not to alarm my wife, slugged the cockroach with a newspaper, put its corpse in a matchbox and took it over to the office. A friendly southern woman opened the door. I could see several other people sitting inside. I told the woman in my most tactful tones that I was sure she had no knowledge of what was going on in her rooms, but, well—I found *this* on our icebox.

The woman burst out laughing and was joined by her guests, who had been listening to me. She gave me a kindly look and said, "Son, if yo' goin' to live in the South, yo'll have to get used to those li'l ol' watah bugs."

That night my wife and I sprayed the kitchen with DDT, closed the kitchen door tight and sat on the other side in the living room swatting escaping cockroaches. We bagged forty-five before the DDT thinned out and they started to go back into the kitchen.

I've found out since that you don't have to get used to cockroaches or anything else in the South if you want to take a bit of trouble to get rid of them. But I didn't know that then. I've also found out since what makes a cockroach so loathsome. I figured it out one night years later in another part of the South. It's because they run so fast. Anything that runs like that when it's caught by surprise gives an impression of evil ways. If it just strolled away, you wouldn't have the same feeling at all. Another thing, of course, is that the cockroach is the only insect that looks over its shoulder to see which way you're coming.

We developed a great yearning to get into the best motel we could find. Our tow-truck friend arranged a ride for us in a car, with all our luggage, to one of the flossiest courts in the South. At that time we were able to get it for only seven dollars a day, and we settled down while the insurance salesman reboahed our cylinders.

It took him ten days to find another motah like mine. The only eating place within walking distance of the court was a swank roadside restaurant with lobsters in the window—the sort of place you save up to go to for somebody's birthday. We ate breakfast, lunch and supper there for ten days, all but breakfast by candlelight, with service from bowing waiters in white jackets.

What about that little camp stove, the one we bought so that we could just stop by the side of the road and cook a snack? I don't know what about it. I hadn't seen it since we took the tablecloth off the toilet seat. Sitting beside a superhighway and cooking a little snack for a family of four is about as probable as running into a swamp girl. And to try to get off some of the six-lane jobs we'd driven on would have meant driving through a guard rail and dropping about eight feet down onto somebody's farm or factory.

It was like that other jovial thought we'd been so fond of back there when we were still starry-eyed about the trip: if the car broke down, we'd just hop a train. When our car broke down, trains were passing us at about ninety miles an hour somewhere, separated from the highway by a couple of hundred feet of jungle.

Every time I phoned the insurance salesman, he said he hadn't found a motah yet, and I had to go back to tipping the waiters in the roadhouse. This went on for ten days. On the morning of the eleventh day I was told over the phone that the car was just about ready and that if I came the next afternoon, I could pick it up.

When I got there the next day, a mechanic was still trying to get the motah back into the car. It was still up in the air, hanging by a block and tackle. He was trying to get the end of the drive shaft into the transmission, uttering a constant strain of soft southern oaths. I watched him for an hour. Everybody who came by took a crack at it. The insurance salesman came around to the garage and tried it, gave up, told me that I'd be so pleased with the new job I'd send him some beaver skins when I got back to Canada and went off chuckling, leaving the motor hanging from the ceiling.

Around nine o'clock that night the mechanic got the motor connected to the rest of the car. The drive shaft went in with a real grand finale of oaths and the sound effects from a violent thunderstorm that had come up suddenly. With perfect timing all the lights in the garage went out. While the mechanic waited for the lights to come on again, he got interested in a fat English bulldog that somebody had brought into the garage. We all stood around a grease pit looking at the bulldog by the light of a flashlight, the dog looking about as happy as I was. The insurance salesman came in, said there was no use trying to finish the job that night and told me if I wanted to I could sleep with the mechanic. I figured that I'd better not leave, or they'd have the motah up in the air again. That night I lay in the dark in a strange room, my spirit of adventure folded up on a chair with my socks, listening to the rain pelt down on the roof while the mechanic, in a bunk a few feet away, puffed on a cigarette in the dark and told me tales about coon hunting.

Next day bright and early everyone went at the motah again. By two in the afternoon the Chevvy was ready to roll. Evidently the mechanic got the wrong pahts from both motahs, because when we finally got it started, it sounded just the way the old motah had sounded just before it broke down.

The insurance salesman told me, "It'll be a bit rough till it gets run-in," charged me $150, and for some reason I'll never understand, I paid him and started off to rejoin my family, wheezing, clanking, heating up and backfiring. I actually made it, by skillful coasting and stopping whenever the radiator started to steam. I averaged about ten miles an hour.

Early next day I set out to see what I could get for my rebuilt Chevvy. It was a bright, hot, sticky morning. The car was boiling nicely by the time I reached the first lot. Used car dealers are naturally pretty cynical, but I've never seen anything quite so depressing as the way they looked that day. I don't pretend to be any more honest than the next guy, but the motor sounded so tough that I figured honesty would be the best policy and told them all exactly what had happened. The Chevvy had suffered a recurrence of an old complaint. The starter would suddenly start to go without my touching it. The motor wouldn't start, but the starter wouldn't stop, no matter what I did. I could turn the ignition off, take the key out or just go for a walk and pretend nothing was happening, but the starter would keep right on with this hysterical moan. The only thing that would stop it was to hit the starter motor with a wrench, which was all the used car dealers needed. One of them offered me a hundred dollars. It was the best offer I got all day.

After the last hopeless call, I was sitting in the car at the curb, wondering what to do, when a gentle-mannered man from Alabama leaned over from the high curb and started to talk to me. He said he'd heard me talking to the used car dealer. He said he'd give me $175 for the car as it stood. I took the offer. This was a day after I'd paid $150 to have the motor rebuilt, which meant a neat profit of $25, if I didn't count what the car was worth in the first place.

This man lived in a little village about twenty-five miles away, and he said he would have to go there to cash a check. I said I'd be glad to drive him. I just got nicely out in the scrub again when the Chevvy started to break down for the second time in two weeks. This car loved to get me between towns.

I pulled over to the shoulder, pulled on the brake, shut off the ignition and said, "Look, there's no point in anybody trying to kid anybody. This car is going to throw another connecting rod if I drive it any farther. I'm not

74

going to drive it another foot. Are you serious about buying it or not?"

My customer looked sad and thoughtful for a minute and finally said he'd give me $125 for it the way it stood and have it towed away. We got out, locked the car and caught a bus to his town. I was beginning to wonder if I'd ever see my wife and kids again.

Transferring ownership proceeded nicely on the assumption that it was a hot car. I got bleak once-overs by cops and damned-carpetbagger looks from notaries public. My Canadian driver's license was scrutinized with narrowed eyes. People muttered excuses and edged away. The man from Alabama was the only one who had faith in me, but finally the deal was closed.

When I went back to the motor court, my wife and I decided that what we really needed was to get a place by the sea and stay there for a little while to get ourselves sorted out and lay plans for the next stage of our adventure— if we could just find a little place by the sea that we could afford.

I've noticed that the suggestions that have had the greatest effect on my life have usually come when I've least expected them, from some little guy leaning against a fence or carrying a crate or unloading a truck or leaning with his head under the hood of a car. That's the way it worked out this time. The second morning after I sold the car, I went for a walk along the highway and saw a little filling station in the shade of a couple of live oak trees. Spanish moss hung from the pumps and an old hound flicked his tail at the sand flies. The proprietor was a small, cheerful, wiry native Floridian with a mahogany-brown face, steel-rimmed glasses, and a fine deep voice out of all proportion to his height. I got talking to him and mentioned our travels and the fact that I hadn't been able to find anyplace that was both within my definition of Florida and within my means. He told me where it was and why.

Something a lot of people don't know about Florida is that the northern half is more of a summer resort than a winter resort. People from the interior, where it gets hot enough in summer to fry you, and from places like Tennessee, Alabama, Georgia and the Carolinas, go to the Florida coast to cool off. As a result, winter is comparatively an off season in the north, and the prices are relatively low. In summer you'd pay more for a third-rate motel in, say, Daytona, than you would in a Miami hotel with a private beach and a room a millionaire rented the winter before for sixty dollars a day. In winter the situation is reversed.

We found a place that most winter visitors drive right through on their way to the land of flamingoes, pink stucco hotels, millionaires and mink. It had a beautiful beach, nothing between us and Africa but the wind and waves and a shore that hadn't changed since it was first seen by Ponce de Leon.

We got a really nice cottage with hot and cold running water, electric lights, electric refrigerator, gas stove and a regular bathroom with a tub. It was right on the dunes, on a little lane behind the palmetto scrub, which was populated by land crabs, lizards, pelicans, mocking birds, and some of the best people I've ever met. The people are still among my closest friends.

I saw the man from Alabama again. He told me he'd bought a brand new motor from Sears, Roebuck for $75, paid $50 to have it installed and had a good little car to hunt squirrels in. He told me that the mechanic who installed the new motor had told him that whoever installed my rebuilt job hadn't even bothered to tighten up some of the bolts on the connecting-rod bearings. I'll always remember what he said when I looked a bit sick and admitted I'd made the wrong decisions about the car all down the line. I liked that guy. He said in his soft, southern voice, "Mistakes?" He looked through his thick glasses out toward the ocean, as if looking a long way back into his past, and said, "Ah've made 'em, son. Man! Have ah made 'em." I felt a lot better. I've often wondered if he's still hunting squirrels in the old Chevvy. I hope so.

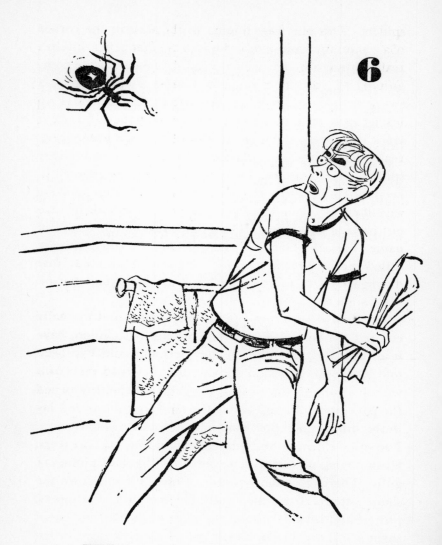

WE settled down to a beach existence and began
to make the acquaintance of some startling forms of animal
life. Here I got my first look at one of those real southern

spiders. This one was clinging to the wall in the corner of a restaurant washroom and was so big that at first I didn't realize it was a spider. When I did, I backed out the door, gulping. I was game, though. I came back and took a swing at it with a rolled-up newspaper. I missed, and we leaped away from each other, me for the door and it for a crack under the molding. It was all a misunderstanding, really, as my wife and I eventually got so used to these spiders, which are completely harmless and are reputed to keep the cottages free of lesser forms of animal life, that we gave them pet names and got to know individuals in various parts of the cottage. I still don't know their technical name. I asked a Floridian one time, and he said, "They're called big ol' *brown* spiduhs." He said it in a way that distinguished them from big ol' red spiders and big ol' black spiders.

But these discoveries kept life interesting, and we really enjoyed the beach. Florida beaches, in my opinion, have it all over anything else on the continent, and I've been told by people who should know that they hold their own with anything in the world. We gathered shells, watched the pale land crabs sail across the sand like ghosts and lay in the sun recuperating from our session with the Chevvy. Porpoises clowned and played tag in the big breakers. Shrimp boats dipped past, accompanied by their plumes of gulls. There was a daily parade of birds up and down the shore: ospreys, ring-billed gulls, herring gulls, sandpipers, plovers and royal terns and the most wonderful soarers of them all, the pelicans, which are so goofy looking when they're grounded but so beautiful when they're air-borne.

Florida seemed to be just about the perfect place to live. There was just one little thing—we hadn't lived there during the summer. The weather had been perfect—hot, but not too hot, breezy and sunny. We discovered, however, that we'd been enjoying a respite from the summer heat. We got a chance to find out what it had been like, because it came back again.

My wife and I began peering doubtfully at each other through the heat waves, wondering which one was going to be the first to crack up. I began wearing shorts all the time. The only change of clothes I made was at night—I took my shorts off. In the morning I put them on again. By ten o'clock I'd be sitting in a deck chair or hip-deep in the ocean, thinking nostalgically of blizzards.

I don't suppose that at any time before or since has there been anyone who perspired as much in Florida as I did. I was literally soaking wet from morning to night, every morning and every night. I remember that one day in town I met a young man and his wife, a lively pretty girl, who burst out laughing when she saw me. I didn't know what the joke was, although I suspected that it was the way I looked in shorts. It turned out, however, that she thought *I* was playing a joke, that I had either stepped under a shower or someone had turned a hose on me, shorts and all. It was a rather awkward moment when I had to explain to her that the water was just me, being turned gradually inside out by the good Florida sun.

There's nothing worse for a northerner, no matter how much he hates snow, than to be hot and perspiring, with sand flies biting him at the same time. When it gets so hot that after biting him they stick to his perspiration, too exhausted to get their feet loose, and just die there in the wee hole they've punctured, he begins thinking of little else than ski slopes.

80

For all that, there was a tropical charm about the weather. The sunrises and sunsets were like something from another world, and the effect of palm and palmetto scrub and deep blue sky was often enough to make us forget the heat. But the heat began to affect the kids. They began to come into the house, walk silently to their beds and just fall flat on their faces and remain there until suppertime. Jane began to get so pale and drawn-looking that we finally took her to a doctor.

He sat behind his desk in his shirt sleeves, fanning himself. His tie was undone, and he looked as if he'd been poleaxed. We told him about Jane's losing weight.

He pulled himself upright slowly, peered closely at Jane, took a few soundings and fell back into his chair again.

"Nothin' wrong with that child, Ma'am," he told my wife, "except she's too hot." He added thoughtfully, "And so am ah."

My wife and I began to realize that this sort of weather had been going on since around April and wasn't over yet and that the same thing would happen every year. It was probable, we reasoned, that if I were going to be a self-employed writer, we'd be able to escape the summer by going north for a month or two each year. But we were looking for a permanent home, where we could live indefinitely, and we didn't want to settle down in a place that we had to escape from a couple of months every year, since some time we might not be able to escape.

We decided that we hadn't quite found the Perfect Place to Live, and we started talking about it again, wondering just where it was. Only now, instead of just talking about it to each other, we talked about it to anyone who would listen, asking their advice. Everyone was glad to join the

81

game of trying to find it for us, including some hot people from Deland who told me one night, with a faraway look in their eyes, that they'd always felt that the ideal place to live was Canada, where you needed a blanket at night and could live just the way you wanted to live, in a log cabin beside a little lake, maybe shooting a moose for lunch or something like that—nothing fancy, but, by God, you'd be doing what you wanted to do.

But the guy who finally won the contest of picking out our future home was a shy, smiling, quietly profane carpenter with ash-blond hair, who was working on a new motel near us. He claimed that the best climate in the world was Flagstaff, Arizona, his home town. I don't know why we settled on his advice, unless it was because of the force of his English.

This guy must have really been homesick, for he neglected to tell us that Flagstaff was over a mile above sea level, that it was the most dependable winter sports center in the southwest and was located fourteen and a half miles from the Arizona Snow Bowl. He just said, with a timid smile, that it was the best God-damned place to live in the whole God-damned world and went on nailing up two-by-fours, whistling "I'm Dreaming of a White Christmas" between his teeth. We were left to head for the Snow Bowl in our beach togs, as we'd blithely sold all our winter clothes, along with our house and toboggans, before leaving Canada.

But we didn't learn about Flagstaff winters till later, when we were involved in a long train trip via Eastern Seaboard to New Orleans, Union Pacific to Houston, and Santa Fe to Flagstaff.

If there's one thing that brings a wan smile to my face,

it's those ads of travelers standing with a hand thrust casually into the pocket of a well-cut suit, watching the approach
of a smiling redcap. Or one of those movie scenes where an
unruffled man-about-town half turns toward the door of
his hotel room and tosses a quarter to a grateful bellhop,
who sweeps it out of the air and salutes, all in one gesture.
When I stand waiting for a redcap, I'm trying to memorize
his features so that I'll be able to identify him later when
he has put my bag on the wrong train. And any time I toss
a quarter, I find myself, after I've given the bellhop another
one, on my hands and knees trying to fish it out from under
the dresser. Tossing quarters accurately requires poise and
confidence, and mine has all gone by the time I've found
out what track my train is on. The rest of the time I travel
with about as much poise as the man they chase between
boxcars and packing crates in the last reel of a mystery
thriller, trying to find the dining car, my luggage, my family, my tickets and someone who knows where my train is.

But what causes me most trouble is my luggage. If red-
caps would just keep their hands off it and let me haul it
around myself, it would arrive at the same place I did at
the same time. But whenever a redcap gets hold of my
luggage, I lose both. If I follow the traveler's maxim,
"Never take your eyes off your luggage," I lose my train and
my family.

One time on this trip we had to change trains at night,
and we had just a half-hour to make the change from one
station to another across town. A redcap grabbed my bags
and put them on a truck and headed down a ramp. I yelled
at my wife, above the din of departing and arriving trains
and escaping steam, not to move from where she stood beside the track and chased the redcap to find out where he

was taking my bags. I had a last glimpse of my wife and family standing at the head of the ramp surrounded by steam. They looked as if I were seeing them at a seance. I trotted along beside the redcap, asking him exactly where I'd pick up my bags. I trotted right down the ramp and turned along a main passageway before I had all the information straight. Then I started back for the ramp and discovered that there were about fourteen ramps, all coming into the same passageway from different tracks and all looking exactly alike. My wife and family were standing at the top of one of them. All I had to do was pick the right one and do it in time to catch a train about six miles away across a strange city. It was like a gigantic shell game, in which my family was hidden under one of the shells. Something else I hadn't noticed as I came down was that there was a guard posted at the bottom of each ramp to prevent people from going up.

I made a wild guess and started for one of the ramps. The guard stopped me, explaining patiently, "The train up there isn't going anywhere. It just got in." I yelled, "I know. I was on it," and tried to fill him in briefly on all the things that had been happening to me. While he tried to figure it all out, I did an end run around him and barged up the ramp. To this day I don't know how I did it, but I picked the right one on the first try.

And, of course, added to my normal confusion about my luggage was the fact that we were traveling with children, who are like luggage with legs. A remark that's made almost as often as the one about our forefathers struggling across the country is the one that's made about travel and children: "It's so educational!" People used to say to us,

84

before we set out, "The children will see things they'll be able to look back on the rest of their lives."

But in spite of this widely accepted notion and those posters that show children peering happily out of train windows at the Grand Canyon, children are not really interested in things like the Grand Canyon—at least not children two and five years old. What children are interested in are cup dispensers, drinking fountains, candy and other kids. Any memories they bring back they could have acquired in their back yards at home. Of all the wonders of nature my kids saw on this trip, Mary remembers one time a little boy squirted some water on her, and Jane remembers a man who gave her a chocolate bar. Neither of them remembers where either event happened. I am the one who remembers what the kids did. Some of the things I remember the way I remember nightmares about finding myself on a streetcar without any clothes on.

Far more memorable than the Grand Canyon in travel with children are things like toilet routines, although the word routine, implying some sort of schedule, is about as misleading as a word can be. Children travel in a little social island. There's their mother, their father and whatever they happen to feel like doing. They usually feel like doing it while you're standing on the platform by track number seven out of New Orleans, surrounded by luggage, carrying coats, dolls, parcels and miscellaneous paraphernalia and wondering whether you should be on track number six.

I've already told about trying to find a bathroom in the American Consulate. I've also searched for bathrooms in such improbable places as pioneer museums, an abandoned gold mine, Grauman's Chinese Theatre, Niagara Glen, The Fountain of Youth, North America's oldest street and the corner of Sunset and Vine. Even when you can find bathrooms, your troubles aren't always over. Taking children to the toilet on a train, for instance, is something like trying to do a waltz in a hammock. Whoever designs those little nooks must get a thousand-dollar bonus for every cubic inch of space he saves. But I'll say this, the kids love them. To a kid, a session in a train toilet combines all the pleasures of being given a piggy-back ride, playing house and going paddling.

There are other, less tangible, reasons why children and travel don't mix. Much of the joy of traveling is the novelty of moving in a pleasant, phony world of finger bowls, string orchestras, deep carpets and bowing waiters. Children affect that atmosphere about the way a case of hives affects a honeymoon. Take ordering meals, for instance. A child-less couple, by means of a certain blank stare, can carry it off in the most exotic eating places, and even give the impression that they recognize the French dishes. With children along, ordering is done while holding the kids apart with one hand, catching toppling water glasses with the other, explaining that you can't buy bubble gum in the best restaurants and asking suave waiters with accents where the toilet is.

I'll never forget one dinner we had on the trip out. This train wasn't the kind where you often find a modest family of four. It was patronized by tall, sun-tanned women in dark glasses and men who wore suits that look the way mine do only when they're being shown to me in style catalogues. Everyone looked like a celebrity. If I'd been traveling alone I might have been able to pass for a character actor.

Traveling with my kids, I more often just looked like a character. It's hard to look sophisticated when you're always having milk spilled on you.

After our first glance into the mulberry-plush-upholstered dining car, my wife and I made up our minds to eat cheese sandwiches for the rest of the trip. Later, when we'd given way to thoughts of a full-course meal, we wished we hadn't changed our minds.

About halfway through the meal, Mary put her chin on her chest, sank lifelessly back into her chair and all but skidded under the table. She said she didn't want her coddled eggs. She not only said she didn't want them, but she dragged them down with her onto her lap and watched them with revived interest as they slithered onto the broadloom carpet.

From then on, our little corner began to sound and look like the kitchen table at home. There's a point of no return in being embarrassed. Once past it, nothing seems to matter. We passed it and just looked back at people and sneered.

I remember one man with a pink bald head and a pince-nez who faced us across the aisle—a solid, composed character who represented everything that is sane, rational and dignified about the human race. He was going over some sales reports or something while he had his dinner. Every now and then he glanced with mild curiosity under our table, where I roamed around on my hands and knees looking for buns and things. I began staring back at him till he went back to his reports. I don't know whether he really decided that it was rude to stare at me or whether he was afraid I was going to bite his leg.

The whole thing came to a climax when Jane, who had

87

been trying to hold her glass to her lips with one finger pressed against the bottom, spilled her milk. Instinctively I reached under the table and slapped her on the bare leg. She let fly with a startled scream that would have made Tarzan put on his pants and go back to being Lord Greystoke. Everybody in the diner froze into stunned silence. Movie stars, or women who looked like movie stars, stopped talking halfway through words and sat there with their mouths open looking as if they'd been caught by a candid camera.

My wife, realizing that she now not only had to manage the children but manage me, turned pink and in a polite whisper called me a mad beast, and we got into one of the weirdest fights we've ever been in, smiling and nodding to each other across the table and telling each other we wished we'd married somebody else. My wife finally got up, took the kids by the hand, gave everyone a haughty sweep of her eyes and went back to our car. I slunk out a few minutes later, feeling like Jack the Ripper.

Another thing you'll often hear is that it's wonderful the way children make friends for you when you're traveling. Wonderful is putting it mildly. They do it by standing in the aisle and staring until the person they're staring at looks over at you and gives you a ghastly smile. I remember one guy my kids picked to stare at. He obviously wanted to read the paper, but he got so nervous that he reached out in a sort of nervous reflex and poked his finger into Mary's stomach, hoping it would put an end to it. Mary started to cry, standing there wet and red-faced, still staring at the poor guy, who went into a frantic routine of jiggling his watch, wiggling his ears and offering us embarrassed explanations. For the rest of the trip he was afraid that if he

88

didn't take any notice of Mary, we'd think he didn't like her and really had taken a poke at her, which by now he wished he had. We were afraid that if we made Mary stop staring at him, he would think that we thought he deliberately tried to make little girls cry, until we all felt like just getting off the train. A distraught sort of acquaintance was struck up, but if that's friendship, I don't want any of it.

Another wonderful thing about the way children make friends for you is the people they choose. Our kids made for us some of the most wonderful friends we've ever seen. One of them was a man with a small red head and no neck who turned out to be a numbers racketeer. He spent the rest of the trip trying to convince me that only bums worked.

One friendship Mary made for us was with a thin, elderly lady on her way to Los Angeles. This friendship started one day when Mary refused to eat. When Mary refused to eat at home, we simply let her go hungry till she changed her mind. But this woman had a whole bag of tricks on how to make kids eat. She hadn't used them since her own family had grown up, but she remembered them all. These tricks consisted of games about little men running up and down Mary's throat, stories about little girls who didn't grow up or grew into monsters without mouths, snatches of songs and imitations of swooping airplanes holding spoons.

If there was anything Mary loved, it was to have something like this going on during her meal. Every day from then on, she refused to eat a spoonful until this woman came over and went into her act. Even the woman began to look as if she would have liked to belt Mary one. But to disguise her feelings, she'd just stand there, waving a spoonful of cereal and telling us about the time she used to make her living examining coconut-fiber mats in a factory in Milwaukee. I still know just how to make coconut-fiber mats.

All in all, traveling with children is something that just makes a normally disorganized experience more disorganized, and my advice is to let them get their education at home. Most of the joys of travel are lost on youngsters anyway. Children take their own world along with them wherever they go. They start in any part of the world exactly where they left off at home. Put them down in the middle of the Mojave Desert, and they'll immediately try to take some little Navajo kid's toys away from him. The prairies are just something to ride across while staring at strange men who would like to be left alone. Oceans are something that people occasionally put merry-go-rounds beside. Old Spanish architecture is something that reminds them that they want a drink of water. All these things they can enjoy just as well at home which is a good place to leave children.

7

We were somewhere in New Mexico when we learned about Flagstaff winters from a plump young Army wife who was on her way to the coast.

91

"It's wonderful if you like winter sports," she said, jiggling her baby. "I used to go skiing there. It's 6,894 feet above sea level."

I had visions of trying to get my luggage up that high over ice and snow, at the end of a rope. My wife and I decided that we'd better change our plans.

Another woman with a baby got into the conversation, making three women and four kids. I was in the middle, chatting away as if I were at a bridal shower. But by then I was so worried about where we were going that I would have joined the Girl Guides if it would have helped. We all tried to figure out where we were going to live. By now my wife and I were wide open to any suggestion that would get us down to sea level. We didn't want to go right to the coast, as we felt that it would be too tough there to get a place to rent, and the only other place we knew anything about was on top of a mountain.

Finally the second woman suggested that we go to the little desert town a hundred miles from the Mexican border where she had been born and raised. She said she didn't think we'd have any trouble finding a place to rent.

So, after a few consultations with the conductor, we changed trains at five o'clock in the morning. The train we'd been traveling on gave a mournful hoot and disappeared into the desert, leaving us standing in the middle of our luggage getting our first good look at one of those places we'd often talked about back in Toronto, where a writer could live so easily. An Indian in a blanket observed me with about the same expression as the one with which I was observing him, and a couple of buzzards circled around waiting for me to die. But our new train arrived within a half-hour, and we made our connection. That afternoon we got our first glimpse of our new home. It lay in the desert five miles away, blinking back silently at the sun and looking like earth-man's first base of operation on the moon.

It is claimed by some of the inhabitants that this town gets hotter than Death Valley. In the summer the temperature goes up as high as 130° in the shade in the daytime and cools off to 129° at night. Although most places now have coolers of some sort, not so long ago there weren't any. In those days, getting through a desert summer in decent shape depended largely on getting enough sleep at night, which was made almost impossible by the heat. One thing the residents used to do was to fill a tub with cold water and get into it with a big bed sheet. They'd wrap the sopping sheet around themselves, get out of the tub and run for the bed. The trick was to get to sleep before the sheet became bone dry, which took only minutes.

But in winter it's hot and bright in the daytime, with a constantly clear, deep blue sky, and so nippy at night that a fire is necessary most of the time. There's no better weather than a desert winter.

But right at that time we weren't taking much notice of the weather. We all flaked out in a motor court. Both of the kids got some kind of stomach complaint, and the gypsy life, now that we'd been dropped into the middle of the desert with our luggage, began to look entirely different to us than it had back in Toronto. My wife had to stay around the motor court with the kids, and I spent the next week looking for a place to rent, making a few halfhearted attempts to do some writing and smuggling food in to my family. I was observed all the while, I discovered later, by the owner of the motor court and his pretty wife, who tried to figure out just what was going on in number twelve. These two eventually became two of the best friends-in-need we've ever had. At the end of a week, figuring that we were having troubles, they came over to see if there was anything they could do for us, and it was through them that we finally got a place to rent.

This was a huge white frame house that had formerly been a government biological research station. I've never before or since slept in such brightly lighted, aseptic surroundings. My wife and I slept in what had been the lab, and when we went to bed at night and lay there reading with the ceiling light glaring down on us, we looked like two people who had volunteered for tests for snake bite.

This was a comfortable house. The landlord, a brisk little hardware merchant had pointed out its shortcomings honestly, and we were glad to get it. But it was rather an emergency arrangement. It gave us our first experience of something that goes with the carefree life: giving up all the little conveniences and comforts that are acquired only by staying in one place for quite awhile. For instance, one thing I had always enjoyed was reading in the bathtub. This was a habit I'd acquired in my youth, and it was pretty strongly associated with pleasant Sunday mornings of my boyhood when, after all the other members of the family had had their baths, I'd lie in the tub reading the week-end comics or *Rolf in the Woods* until I just had time to show up at the dinner table, scrubbed, shining and holy-looking, to watch my father carve the roast beef.

I would half-fill the tub with hot water, grope my way around through the steam arranging books and magazines at a handy distance from the tub, adjust the temperature of the water until I could just barely stand it then lie there reading and gradually turning pink. As I grew older, various people tried to break me of the habit. The first was my father, a reasonable, calm man who chose the course of casual example. If he mentioned that he was going to have a bath, and someone said, "I'm not sure there's enough hot water," he'd say, in an elaborately calm manner, without even looking at me, "A few inches of water is all I need." A man who pursued an idea with lively imagination and a fondness for hyperbole, he kept making the quantity less and less until it became a sort of psychological game between us: me taking deeper and deeper baths, and my father taking them in less and less water, in his imagination, until he got down to a cupful and finally began saying, "a teaspoonful is all I need," at which my mother would say with some asperity, "For heaven's sake, you must get nice and clean."

After I left home, various people tried to make me stop, telling me that I'd kill myself, fall asleep and drown, be electrocuted, scald myself or have a heart attack. The last was my wife, who eventually became too busy with the children to bother much about it, except to say occasionally, "Why can't you just have a bath like a normal person?"

But what finally broke me of the habit, at least for a long time, was this house in the desert. This place had all sorts of conveniences. It lacked only one thing—a bathtub. The builder presumably had felt that anybody who couldn't get clean in a shower was too dirty to live in a house anyway.

One day I was in the bathroom looking at a broken faucet which the landlord wanted fixed and about which I'd been calling a plumber every day for a week, when I began to take stock of the possibilities for having a bath. I reasoned that I very seldom lay full length in a tub, but lay like the letter "N" on a slant, and that, by skillful arrangement of two washtubs, I could have the same sections of me in the same depth of water as in the most modern built-in job on earth. So when my wife had taken the kids into town to do some shopping, I decided to give it a try. I figured the idea might appear a bit nuts, but I'd be finished and sitting on the porch before my wife got back, and nobody would know anything about it.

I got two washtubs, one regular-sized, and the other slightly smaller and took them into the bathroom along with a big saucepan with which to ladle the water from the shower into the tubs. I got a big beach towel to cover my shoulders when I was in position, as a door led from the bathroom directly outside, and the bathroom was apt to be a bit drafty. In fact, the door had a loose latch and frequently blew open. To be sure that I didn't run out of hot water, I got a kettle of boiling water and placed it under the sink. I gathered together half a dozen magazines and piled them beside the tub. The place was beginning to look a bit like the boiler room of a leaky old ship.

When I settled into position, I managed to spill quite a bit more water and found that to stop the flow I had to sit with my elbows up in the air, as if I were being measured for a vest.

I'm not quite sure yet of the sequence of events after that, but I remember making some motion in the tub that sent an extra amount of water over the side just as my wife, who had finished her shopping earlier than she expected, came in the door and said, "There's water pouring out into the hall." Then, on a rising note, she added, "Bob, are you all right?"

I said, "Yep, fine, just spilled a bit of water." I waited till I heard my wife making the kids a bite to eat then started looking frantically for a way to get the whole mess cleaned up before anybody noticed it. Just then Mary, with unerring instinct for a dramatic situation, announced clearly, "I have to go to the bathroom."

I remember hollering, hardly recognizing my own voice, "You *can't* want to go to the bathroom!"

"I *have* to," Mary repeated calmly.

I got up, swearing and dripping water, some in the tub and some outside of it, knocked the magazines on the floor, wrapped the sodden towel around me and opened the door. Mary took a fascinated look, just before I yanked her off the floor, lifted her over everything and then sank back into the soapy water, towel and all. The two of us sat there looking at each other. I hadn't noticed it when I opened the door, but she was clutching a bologna sandwich. She sat there eating it in a bemused fashion.

I don't know whether I could have passed her out again without my wife seeing the whole mess. But I never got the chance, for there was a knock at the door, the one that opened on the back yard from the bathroom. I heard my wife go to the kitchen window. She called to me, "It's the plumber."

It was then that I panicked, began to holler frantic instructions to my wife, got up, knocking over the empty tub and skidding on wet magazines, wrapped my towel around me and clutched Mary. So that she could hold on to me better, I grabbed her sandwich from her and stuck it in my mouth as the only comparatively dry spot within reach. Then I kicked over the kettle, scalding one foot and sending a sheet of steaming water out under the door. I screamed

97

around the sandwich, and I heard my wife shout, "For *heaven's* sake, have you lost your mind?"

In the commotion, I thought she called to the plumber to go right in, that I wouldn't mind, and in a final breakdown I opened the door into the house to escape, just as my towel slipped into the tub and the suction from the inside door opened the outside door, leaving me standing exposed between the plumber, who was chatting with my wife, and a mountain range about seventy miles to the south.

I'll always remember that scene. There was the desert. And there was I standing in a washtub, holding up a little girl, apparently to no purpose, with a towel floating in the tub, a bologna sandwich in my mouth, and the plumber frozen in the act of licking a cigarette paper. It was an experience that got my mind off hot baths for a long time. From then on I took showers.

For recreation instead of lying in a hot bath I went for walks in the desert—not far enough to lose sight of town when I was on level ground, but far enough that when I'd get down into an arroyo and build a little fire of bits of brush, I could sit there surrounded by such complete silence and motionless, timeless desolation that I'd feel like the First Man. The absence of the sound of birds, insects and rustling leaves can make the desert incredibly silent. I remember one day when I was sitting on a rock at the bottom of an arroyo, I strained my ears for about five minutes, trying to identify a strange ticking sound, until I realized I was hearing the sound of my wrist watch.

My caution about not losing sight of town, a caution so intense that it would have made an old whanghide turn aside and blush for me, was based partly on my own limited experience of the deceptive angles and distances on the desert but chiefly on tales I'd been told by a man with whom I'd struck up a good friendship. He was a Texan who must have discouraged people who like people to conform to type, because he was fat and bland-faced and never stopped talking. I became very fond of him and particularly fond of his stories.

He lived alone in a frame cabin outside town, where he ran into some of the most fascinating experiences I've ever heard of. One night he came home late and walked for about thirty feet along the path to his cabin, kicking with annoyance to get rid of what he thought was a coil of wire caught around his leg, to discover after awhile that it was a sidewinder, one of the most lethal rattlers, which was trying just as hard to get rid of him. It was evidently trying so hard that it forgot to bite him. Another time he got out of bed at night to have a snack of some cookies from a can that, without his knowing it, had been left partly open and was being marauded by ants. He stood there in the dark, happily eating cookies and ants, until he noticed a peculiar warm sensation around his lips, where the ants were biting him as fast as he was biting them. He never entirely got over the experience, and sometimes when an ant crossed the floor in front of him, he would stop halfway through a sentence and watch it in thoughtful silence.

He was in charge of the air-conditioning and heating equipment in the local bank building. He used to take me down among the pipes and give a running commentary on his job. "I've held this job longer than anyone else. You know why? Because I never want to know why I do anything. I just want to know what I'm supposed to do. I keep my mind clear. A man says, you turn that valve a quarter of a turn at eight in the morning, and that's all I want to know. I don't want to know what it does."

He knew the desert and one time had been invited to join a couple of fliers from the East in an air search for a lost mine. They had been forced down by engine trouble, and he told the story as an illustration of the queer way the desert can mix people up in their directions. As soon as they rolled to a stop, the pilot said, "Well, let's get going."

"Get going where?" my friend asked him flatly.

"To the road. The one we flew over just five minutes ago. It's right over there."

The Texan told him that he wasn't moving from the plane. People would be searching for them soon, and he was going to stay right where he was. He'd seen too much of the desert not to know how it could twist directions around. There was an argument. The others thought he was already touched by the sun. But he stuck to his argument and the plane.

"We were picked up eighteen hours later," he told me. "And when we were, this guy was still saying the road was right over there and pointing in the exact opposite direction from the one he'd been pointing when we landed. He got lost just sitting still."

While living in this desert town, I saw my first cowboys at work—two of them, who obviously had never read any western stories, because they had no idea how cowboys should act. The first one was sitting out on the range beside a little fire, eating the biggest piece of white gooey layer cake I've ever seen, with white icing on it about three inches thick. Don't ask me where he got it. He must have packed that cake along on a burro. The second one I saw one day when some friends drove me up toward Nevada. He was

100

standing waving his hat at some steers trying to get them to go up a ramp into a truck. The steers went every way but the right way, until in quiet disgust the man went over and got onto his horse, which he'd tied to a fence post. He did this in exactly the same way a plumber would go to get a wrench. It was an indispensable tool. When he was on his horse, he leaned over and took from a post a neat brown jacket which he put on. He looked a bit like an accountant. He brushed it off fussily and rode into the steers, still as far as I could see, concentrating on his jacket, while his pony matter-of-factly, all on his own, batted all the steers up the ramp with his haunches. It was a very neat and competent bit of work and made me realize that cowboys are very skilled craftsmen.

8

As soon as we got settled down, we started Jane at kindergarten. The first day, wanting to make sure she got home but also wanting her to do it without help, I hid behind a parked car across the road to see what she'd do when she came out of school. She came to the sidewalk, looked carefully north, looked carefully south, then turned to a little Mexican boy and asked him politely, "Where is my home?" How he knew, I don't understand yet, but he answered without hesitation in Mexican, giving complete instructions with his hands, which both Jane and I understood. Jane thanked him, and silently, from my hiding place, so did I.

But Jane went to school only a few hours a day, and Mary hadn't started yet, so most of the time we were all at home together. It became one of the biggest problems of being free and independent and doing what we wanted to do. I'd freed myself from the well-established custom of the man of the house's disappearing each morning and not coming home till suppertime. I became as permanent a domestic fixture as a sewing machine, except that I could move around and bump into my wife. She used to listen in the evening to radio plays about marriages' breaking up because the wife didn't see enough of her husband. My wife had a hard time figuring out what the plot was about. The problem in our marriage wasn't like one of those plays that end with the husband and wife getting to know each other again. The former biological lab in which we were living, although a little on the old side, had been remodeled into something comparable to a modern, functional little bungalow, where the only place to hide was the bathroom. So our life was more like one of those movies where rubber planters marooned by the monsoons begin accusing one another of stealing the teapot.

There were times when my wife and I tried so hard to escape each other that it was like playing in-and-out-the-window. We'd catch ourselves looking at each other, smile briefly, and both head briskly for some other room, as if we'd just thought of something. I'd go to the bedroom, and my wife would go to the kitchen. I'd peek around to see if she were still there and find that she was looking to see if *I* were still there. We'd pretend we hadn't been looking and start back for two other rooms. We'd wriggle our fingers at each other as we passed in the hall and say, "Hi."

I'd go into the bathroom, yank my cheek back, look for cavities, make a catapult of my wife's curlers and shoot little bobby pins at her nail polish. Sometimes I'd recite poetry without making a sound. One time I was reciting, "My Liege, I did deny no prisoners," with gestures, when I caught sight of a plumber who was repairing the eaves trough on the bungalow next door. He was standing on his ladder looking in the window at me. We stood there looking at each other, me pretending I was just going to wipe off the medicine-cabinet mirror with the bowl brush. He backed slowly down, never taking his eyes off me, folded his ladder and left.

Sometimes my wife and I would crack under the strain and start calling each other, asking if we were all right.

"Are you all right?" my wife would call from the kitchen.

"Pardon?" I'd say from behind the bathroom door.

"Just a minute," my wife would say, "till I turn off the tap."

"WHAT DID YOU SAY?" I'd holler.

"I SAID JUST A MINUTE TILL I TURN THE TAP OFF."

"ARE YOU ALL RIGHT?" I'd holler.

I'd stick my head around the bathroom door. My wife would stare at me in alarm.

"Why are you looking at me like that?" I'd say.

104

"I thought you were looking at me."

"I was."

"Are you all right?"

In an average day I became more involved with women, kids and household affairs than a businessman gets in a year. I found out a lot of things that a man never really gets to know ordinarily. For instance, most men suspect that women have no imagination, but it doesn't bother them too much. A guy going downtown to work is away from home all day, and for the length of time it takes to have his evening meal, he has no trouble keeping the conversation three-dimensional, firmly fixed in space and time and confined to things you can paint, plug in, switch off, wear, eat or drive off in. I was at the table three times a day, often trying to warm up the kind of conversation that I used to get into fairly often during coffee sessions with the guys. I usually found myself talking to myself.

I remember that one time, early in my life as a displaced male, I said at the lunch table:

"Do you know that according to the laws of chance any event will happen in an unlimited time. If you chained a monkey to a piano so that he poked the keys for billions of years, he'd eventually play Beethoven's *Ninth Symphony?*"

My wife and daughters looked at me in dead-pan silence. Then Jane turned to her mother and said, "Kathie Baumgartner deliberately stayed out in the hall today because she didn't do her homework."

"If that Linda Tewpis," Mary said, "doesn't stop kicking my doll carriage over, I'm going to punch her."

My wife looked thoughtfully at their little chests. "You'll both have to change your blouses tomorrow," she said.

"LOOK! For the—!" I squealed. "Does anybody happen

105

to recall that I just made a statement about mathematics?"

My wife brought me into focus. "I thought you were just being funny," she said. "I didn't know you asked me anything."

"I just happened to mention one of the most staggering concepts of the human brain," I told her.

"I thought you were talking about a monkey."

"I was talking about mathematics—not monkeys."

"If you're going to start roaring, let's just drop the subject," my wife said.

"DROP it," I yelled. "We haven't even picked it UP yet."

"May I be excused?" Jane said.

I whipped around at her, "NO, YOU MAY NOT! You may sit there and listen to your mother and me have a friendly discussion."

"For heaven's sake," my wife said, "get it over with. *What was it about a monkey?*"

Getting enthusiastic about an abstract subject around three women of any age is like stepping on a rake in a dark driveway.

I'd say something like, "I wonder if we all see the world the same way. Maybe what you call red is different from what I call red."

"How could it be," my wife would say, "if it's red?"

"Well, I mean, maybe when I say, 'That coat is red,' maybe to me it looks green, only I call green red."

"That reminds me," my wife would say. "That coat of yours should go to the cleaners. It makes you look like the man in those ads, who didn't take out insurance."

To be perfectly fair, I don't think it's exactly that a woman *has* no imagination. What makes her keep snapping back to earth as if she were attached to it by her hosiery supports is that she just can't disassociate ideas from people.

A woman never attacks a question. She attacks the person who asked it, with little verbal egg lifters and banana peels.

"If a man and a turtle started a race," I said one day, when I was full of the paradoxes of Zeno, which I'd been reading, "and the man could run ten times faster than the turtle but started ten feet behind it, he could never catch the turtle. By the time the man had run ten feet, the turtle would have run a foot. By the time the man had run a foot, the turtle would have run a tenth of a foot. You just keep dividing by ten to prove the man will never catch him."

I could mention this to any four guys, any time, from morning coffee to a late beer, and half of them would at least sit there thinking about it for awhile. The other half would take out their pencils and start doing algebra.

My wife looked at Jane, frowned, jerked her shoulders back in a signal for Jane to straighten up, slapped Mary's elbow off the table, folded her hands in her lap, looked at me for a moment until she remembered what I said, then remarked, "Of all the men in the world, I had to marry one who believes a man can't run as fast as a turtle."

I closed my eyes and slapped my forehead. *"Believe it!"* I chanted. "What difference does it make whether I *believe* it? What's wrong with the reasoning, that's what I want to know?"

When I opened my eyes, my wife had turned pink.

"You're so smart," she said, "but when I left you to put the stew on to simmer today, you took it off, turned the back burner on full and set the tea cosy on fire."

"What—! What's that got to do with what we're talking about?"

"Because you think that I'm stupid, but you think a man can't catch a turtle."

"I *don't* think a man can't catch a turtle."

"Then why are you trying to prove it?"

"BECAUSE IN THEORY A MAN CAN'T CATCH A TURTLE."

"Oh, in theory."

Women use the word "theory" the way I use the word bum.

I found that a woman just isn't interested in what's going on inside her head, or inside anyone else's. It's almost impossible for her to imagine herself in someone else's shoes. It makes her look a bit cold-blooded at times. Actually she's not to blame. A man can identify himself with his fellow creatures, because he can afford to spread his compassion as thinly as he wants. A woman has to pile it thick in one place, her home. A single session with the kids exhausts the average guy's supply of love in about an hour and a half.

Nevertheless a woman's attitude to her fellow humans is something that often leaves a man feeling as if he'd been sitting in a slight draft. During this period my bank account was disappearing fast, and I had to do some fancy juggling at times to keep my finances straight. I had a couple of accounts still active back in Toronto, on which I was still making payments. Whenever I wrote to the credit managers about my troubles, they'd be fascinated. I often wrote to one man whom I'd known for years in Toronto, a little man with a small, white face and a lot of black hair, who used to sit surrounded by about two hundred women with needle-sharp pencils, white cuffs, spike heels and adding machines. He looked forward to my letters like a new installment on an adventure story.

I used to tell him of wild financial trails, overgrown with overdue checks, of hacking my way through second notices as brilliantly colored as orchids and eerie bogs of carrying charges. I'd tell him I was working on an article on owls and another on life after death, and would it be all right if I sent him $80 two weeks from next Wednesday?

I'd always get a letter back from him wishing me luck and saying that he was working on a book about poison mushrooms himself, and two weeks would be satisfactory.

Every now and then I'd try this on some other company with a woman credit manager. I'd get a letter back that said, "Yours of the thirteenth received about your article on owls. Please send check for $87.37 by return mail."

The people of a woman's world occupy two spheres. There are the members of her family, with whose troubles she can identify herself with a compassionate imagination unattainable to man. And there's the rest of the world, made up of a lot of things with faces.

But the main discoveries I made about women were about my wife, who was in turn making discoveries about me which often left her longing for a husband who would kiss her good-by at eight-thirty and hello at five.

One thing that threw me for a loop was women's hair. With a man, hair is just something to get cut off when he begins to notice a peculiar nuzzling feeling at the back of his neck every time he looks up from his work. He steps out in the morning, gets into a barber's chair, says, "The

109

usual, Joe," picks up the magazine with the best cheesecake on the cover, reads an article, says, "S'long, Joe," and gets back to worrying about the gas bill.

With a woman hair isn't a substance, it's a situation. A permanent crisis. At this moment there isn't a woman in North America who isn't just getting over a permanent or just waiting for a permanent or thinking of having her hair done, undone, or piled on top. It's a series of recurring assaults with, in between, periods of research and discussion, reassembly of confederates and elaborate planning.

When my wife got ready for a hairdo, she'd start by announcing, "I'm going to have my hair done two weeks from Tuesday. You'll have to look after the children."

Well, I'd figure, I could face anything in two weeks. I'd say okay. My wife would start looking in the mirror. She would hold her hair up as if trying to pick herself off the floor, stick pins into it, frown, lift up strands and look undecided.

The big day would arrive. I'd be left alone with the can opener, some beans, pea soup and a list of instructions about sending Jane to school in the white blouse with the blue trim and not letting Mary near any mud. I'd think of my wife out there Facing the Situation—Alone. I'd be a bit uneasy.

At six she'd come in. There would be a warning look in her eyes as she went straight to the bedroom mirror. I'd keep my fingers crossed. I'd know better than to go in. She would come out into the kitchen and look me right in the eye.

"Well, how do you like it?"

"It looks nice," I'd say. "Sort of fuzzy."

110

My wife would burst out crying. "I'll sue him," she'd say.

She'd go back to the mirror and stand there sobbing and holding the strands out one by one, like spaghetti.

I tried to get over to the woman's point of view, but I found I didn't even speak the language. I'd read in a magazine how women with hourglass-shaped faces should have bell-shaped bangs. I'd figure maybe my wife hadn't seen it, and at supper I'd light a cigarette and tell her about it.

My wife would look at me as if I'd just got mud on the carpet. "Will you give me fifty dollars a month to keep my hair done in bell-shaped bangs? It's all I can do to get my housekeeping allowance away from you."

"What's fifty bucks got to do with it?"

"Those hairdos are all right for a woman who has curls that will stay flat," she'd say.

The whole business seemed full of secret meanings only women understood. It was a sort of world-wide, but rigidly exclusive, club in which the membership requirements were that you must be a woman and have hair.

Our next-door neighbor, a noisy young mother of twins, from Houston, would come in to see my wife, her head done up in curlers, looking like a pineapple. Knowing how pretty she was normally, I'd run to offer her a quick drink, when my wife would say, "Oh, Lois. It just suits you."

I'd expect Lois to walk out livid with rage, but she'd smile and look pleased.

The next time, Lois would come in with her hair looking the way women's hair should look, soft and loose, without curlers. My wife would say, "Oh, well, it will grow in again. But I'd never go back to him."

111

When Lois had gone, I'd say, "What's the matter? I thought it looked kind of nice."

"Looked nice!" my wife would say scornfully. "For how long? He's cut off all the ends. The poor girl!"

Another day Lois would come home from a hair job, and my wife would rush out onto the porch to have a look. This time everybody would be happy. My wife would say it looked lovely. Lois would think it looked lovely. I'd think it looked lovely. I'd smile and relax. Everything would seem settled. Lois would say, "See you later," and after supper come in with it all up in curlers.

After, when I'd mention it to my wife, she'd say, "You didn't expect it to stay that way without being set, did you?"

Often when I was working, I looked out my window and saw as many as three women at one time slipping into one another's houses as if they were engaged in a weird sort of musical chairs, except that they were playing it with ranch houses, all with towels over their shoulders, bristling with curlers, papers, wrappers, pin curls, combs and everything but tire irons. Without any noticeable sign or introductory remark, they'd all call to one another things like: "Next time I'm going to have a pompadour on top."

I made one try at getting to the bottom of the mystery. One day my wife went to the hairdresser. When she came home, she said, "Well, I go to the hairdresser next Tuesday."

I sat there thinking, am I going nuts or is there really something about this I don't understand? I said slowly, "Look, weren't you—at—the—hairdresser's—today?"

"I didn't get a permanent. I just got a finger wave," she said.

"Why didn't you get a permanent?"

"It's too short."

"How did it get that short?"

"I just had it cut," my wife said, as if wondering what made men so dense.

"Why?" I asked, fighting all the way.

"To cut some curl off it," she said.

I ankled off to do some work on the car (a cheap job recently acquired and later sold in Pasadena) and tried not to think about it any more, telling myself, after all, my wife has been driving a car for over a year without having any idea of what's under the hood. Maybe I can get along with a woman without understanding what's under *her* hood.

9

TRAVEL is supposed to be a wonderful thing not only for children (it's so educational) but for writers, who, according to the popular notion, have to get around and see all sorts of things to have something to write about.

This worked in reverse for me. When I lived in Toronto, I wrote stories about mountain climbing in the Alps and big-game hunting in Africa, most of which ended with storms and didn't sell any better than the ones that ended with fires. Now that I was living in the middle of the desert, surrounded by mountains, rattlesnakes, prospectors, Navajos, Mojaves, cowboys and white-faced Herefords, I wrote a story about a man in my home town who stuffed birds and I sold it. I also wrote an article recommending that people stay home and sold that too. This was the peak of my career. I made $450 in nine months, or slightly more than a good sitter, then folded up.

Anyway, I got so busy writing letters that I hardly had time to write anything else. This is a problem of going to the Perfect Place to Live: you have to write thousands of words back home to the people who didn't go there. A mathematical law works against the one away from home. If you want to keep in touch with, say fourteen friends, each of whom writes once a week, you have to write two letters a day. This doesn't sound much until you miss a few days.

My wife and I were sometimes as busy with our correspondence out there among the sidewinders as two debutantes at the opening of the social season. We often worked so late that we began sending out those labored efforts that go, "Things are about the same at my end and hoping you are the same at your end." We grew bleary-eyed staring at little words like "took," "tooke," "tuk," which we wrote out on separate pieces of paper to find out what suddenly made them look queer, like husbands.

But more than offsetting the effort was the pleasure of

hearing from our friends, which was one of the best things about living away from home. Many of them wrote a lot better stuff than I was writing for editors, and it was sometimes intriguing to study the various approaches to letter writing. I used to like particularly to read the letters my wife got from an English girl friend, who larruped right in with low shoes, a lot of feeling and a conviction that the things that were happening inside her were far more interesting than the things that were happening outside her. She'd write:

My Dear: Please don't think me too beastly for not writing sooner, but life is such a bore at times that one finds that one simply can't face writing one's friends, then one finds oneself suddenly walking in the country and thinking of something simply heavenly with red sideburns and a little moustache. . . .

And I used to love to hear from a niece of mine in Sarnia, who would write:

Dear Uncle Bob: I fell in the river yesterday. I like being wet. Sally had four more kittens. I saw a skunk. Joan won't let me play with her doll. I hope she dies. I hope you are well. Love . . .

I also got letters from a man who wrote about something I'd said in my story about stuffing birds and with whom I struck up a gruff but friendly correspondence. I used to picture him sitting amid books and old dinosaur bones with a pipe clamped between his teeth, surrounded by the smell of good tobacco and ideas. He would grumble:

Dear Allen: Darwin said that the horse, ass, zebra, quagga and haemonius were all evolved from an equine animal striped like the zebra but differently constructed and that the ancestors of all domestic animals. . . .

And through my one article, I had my first contact with one of those people who write mysterious, cranky letters to editors, frequently quoting Chaucer or someone who sounds like Chaucer.

Dear Allen: I've just finished your garbage about travel. Obviously you want to be a movie star. Why don't they? As if you didn't know. Oh well—
>"I'll fit sonne gonyan day,
>Thou saydest eek, that there
>Been thinges thre. . . ."
>In disgust . . .

But getting letters from our friends had become one of the most vital things in our lives, as Christmas was only a few weeks away, and we were getting properly homesick. To make matters worse, we went to hear a children's choir in one of the stores. We listened to "O Holy Night" and "Hark! the Herald Angels Sing," standing in the washtub department, with the desert sand whispering against the windows and the tears pouring down our faces. Lean ranch hands in blue jeans walked around us buying blowtorches and things, and a fierce-looking Navajo family watched us, obviously thinking if the white man got any softer, the Indians would have the country back in no time.

But Christmas was livened up by the kids, who didn't care where they spent it as long as they got some toys, and by an expedition to a near-by mountain for a Christmas tree. I went with my Texas friend, who ended up in a dire scene with the owner of some ranch land, both of them making veiled threats about who could shoot the other

117

faster, something that got my mind off the fact that I was homesick.

We stayed in the desert until the temperature went up to 117° in the shade, and our front doorknob, which was in the sun, was so hot that I began letting myself into the house by putting my hand in my pocket, standing on tiptoes and wrapping the knob in a handful of my pants.

We decided that it was time to go home, take stock of all we'd seen and decide where we were going to live.

"After all," we told each other, our eyes glowing at the thought of moving again, "that was the original idea."

But first we wanted to see the coast. We were all packed and ready, and on our last day in the desert I went down to the bank building to see my Texas friend, who looked after the machinery in the basement. As I approached the building, I noticed a lot of activity outside. Workmen were busy tearing up a big strip of roadway, and there was a lot of water around. I went into the bank and was told I could find my friend at the lunch counter across the street. I found him having a cup of coffee. He looked very sad.

"Remember all those valves I showed you?" he said, without expression. "Turned the wrong one last night. Let a hundred and eighty-five pounds pressure into the wrong line. Blew up fifteen feet of sidewalk."

I haven't seen him since. I hope he is happy and working at something that doesn't have valves.

Next day we drove across the remaining desert that separated us from the coast. Very little of the North American desert has those sand dunes they use in movies about sheiks and German spies. A great portion of the desert is about like a sandy city lot on which a brick building has been torn down, with coarse shrubs rooted in the rubble at distances of twenty or thirty feet, causing the desert to look green from a low angle. Multiply that picture a few million times, add barren mountains, sprinkle with cactus, stir well until everything is cracked and fissured and warm considerably before serving, and you have a rough idea of some of the terrain we drove through that day.

Late that afternoon we reached the coast. We rented a snug little ranch house in Pasadena, owned by a man who had gone in for taxidermy, and settled down for a month amid china cabinets full of stuffed owls to discover how we liked the California that most people think of as California —the land of palms, red-tile roofs, swimming pools, blondes, muscles and flowers. When my wife saw it she began to wonder whether we should go home after all, even for a visit. Here was a sunny, snowless civilization, with cool nights, razzle-dazzle shopping districts and supermarkets like the foyer to heaven. Maybe this was The Place.

My wife was more enthusiastic than I was. I found it hard to see past those formal gardens and shrubs shaped like wieners. I've never liked cultivated flowers; to get me into a flower show has always been like trying to give a dog a bath. And here I was in the biggest flower show on earth, with green wieners added and the whole thing accompanied by the tinkling, unreal music of the Good Humor Man, which used to float faintly through my window to me at night like something coming from under a distant toad-stool.

My wife and I often stood peering out windows, one looking east and the other west, and my wife frequently got a look in her eye as if weighing me against Pasadena and

trying to keep from laughing. But the children needed a
father. Or did they?

Now we not only weren't sure where we wanted to live
but whom we wanted to live with. The kids, in the meantime, oblivious of everything, including California, quietly
played with the snails they found under the green wiener
trees.

When I wasn't looking at the stuffed owls, I sat with my
fingers poised over my typewriter, looking out onto a de-
ceptively quiet street, the lone spectator of a nether world
of mayhem, treachery and propaganda, as the preschool-age
children were turned outdoors, one by one, their little faces
wiped clean of toast crumbs and their souls full of diabol-
ical plans. They passed my window all day long, in thin-
column formation, in a perpetual state of spine-chilling,
dead-pan, passionless war. They wore hunting caps, long
pink nightgowns, their mothers' shoes and lace curtains.
Sometimes they moved by on wheels, sometimes on foot,
but they all had one objective: to frame one another.

By lunchtime each day things had become so snarled that
it was impossible to tell who was telling the truth. Right
and wrong got so balled up in one gumbo mixture of bubble gum and tricycles that none of the mothers could sort
them out, even if they'd wanted to. They just didn't worry
about it.

One day I watched two little boys with shaved heads ride
around a tree on their tricycles, slowly and aimlessly, from
eight in the morning till suppertime, telling each other in
agitated voices that they'd break each other's tricycles, that
they'd climb up onto lampposts and drop rocks on each
other's heads, that they'd put each other in jail. Around
eleven o'clock, one of them got off his trike, went over and

hit the other in the mouth, then went home hollering, "Mummy! Pete hit me."

His mother came out, looked at him sharply, said, "Pull your pants up," and went back in.

Two strange little boys meeting for the first time would stand looking into each other's faces for a moment, then start conscientiously kicking each other until one started howling and went home.

Little tots with legs like noodles toddled off each morning in pigtails, bows and pocket-size dresses, on their way to play a day-long game, the object of which was to try to get somebody else spanked. When they scored, they all stood around sucking popsicles, watching. They didn't laugh or gloat or show any excitement. Their faces would be completely expressionless.

Every other minute they'd go and tell their mothers. If they didn't have anything to tell them, they made something up. Sometimes they told their own mothers, sometimes they told the other kid's mother. If they couldn't find either mother, they told the breadman. It was a peculiar world, where the idea seemed to be that if you could stay with it until everyone was grown up, it would all sort itself out.

One day a little girl with a head of white curls let out a nerve-shattering scream that brought six mothers racing from their doors, three of them in curlers.

"Doris! What *is* it!" gasped one of them.

Doris put her hand on her flat little chest, looked across a geranium hedge at another little girl and said in a hoarse stage whisper, "Gail looked at me!"

"It's time you came in for lunch, anyway," her mother said.

One afternoon three little girls were playing. Suddenly two of them pushed the third off the veranda, then picked up her doll, threw it at her and kicked over a house she'd made out of old cartons. I was almost ready to leap up from my typewriter and cross the road to lecture them on the rudiments of justice, sportsmanship and the Geneva Conference. The little girl who had been shoved off the veranda screamed. The other two screamed back at her. The woman of the house came out.

"They broke my house," the little girl wailed.

"Why did you break Susan's house?" the woman asked, mechanically retying a bow.

"We were through playing with it," one of them said.

"Pull up your socks," the woman said, "and don't get dirty."

One time I listened to one youngster ask in a flat monotone, at intervals all morning, if another would let her play with her doll carriage.

"Can I have your carriage?" she'd say.

"No."

At noon the mother of the kid with the carriage put her head out the door and called her daughter in for lunch. The youngster put the top of the carriage up, started home and fell down the veranda steps. She lay on her back, reaching for a sound proportionate to the fall. I could hear the scream coming like water working its way up to the nozzle of a garden hose. Just before it arrived, the other kid, who stood looking down at her like a little gangster in pigtails, evidently figuring that she was going to die, said, "Can I have your carriage now?"

Evidently mercy is something that begins to show itself

122

around voting age. Jane, who although going to school was still young enough to retain the preschool spirit, would chatter away at lunch, telling about the things that had happened at school.

"There's a boy in our class named Johnny," she said one day, industriously spooning chicken-noodle soup into herself. "He talks all the time."

"M-hm," I said.

"This morning the teacher said, 'Well, I'm going to put you in the middle of four good little girls, Martha, Joan, Dianne and Jane.'"

"So?"

"'And if you talk,' she said, 'I'm going to ask Martha, Joan, Dianne and Jane to tell me, and I'm going to send you to the office.' We had great fun."

"How do you mean?"

"We tried to get him to talk so we could tell the teacher."

"You what!" I brought her into focus, as it dawned on me what she'd said.

"We tried to see how we could get him to talk," she said, getting up to get some more soup.

My wife said, "Oh, Jane. You shouldn't!"

"Shouldn't what?" Jane said in surprise.

"Shouldn't take more soup," my wife said.

I discovered that in the world of women and children, promises and systems of ethics are held together lightly by a thin coating of orange juice and hair fix and an occasional safety pin. It often left me wishing that I were back amid the jolly cutthroat atmosphere of big business. There people did one another in according to firm principles. At home nobody would have recognized a principle if she'd

123

found it in her shredded wheat. It amounts to the same thing, probably, but it's easier on the nerves when it doesn't take place on a quiet, sunny street.

In fact, if I'd been downtown instead of sitting like an old possum at my typewriter, watching everything that was going on, some of the things that happened wouldn't have occurred. I decided that I'd straighten out some of the little adventures in misunderstanding around my own house with a few Solomon-like decrees. It was something like someone who has been smoking a flat fifty cigarettes a day for twenty years giving it up in favor of contemplating cosmic truths. It's a wonderful idea, but if he tries it too suddenly, he'll end up being chased around by a man with a net.

At this time Mary, who was toddling around with a face as guileless as a carving off a harp, started using what the psychologists call naughty words. I can't tell you the word Mary favored, but it was one used usually on dead car batteries.

But I ignored it, on the principle that if we paid no attention, she'd forget it, and she went on using it regularly —on her dolls, building blocks and the little windmills she made out of her Tinker Toys. It was like watching a Little Golden Book version of *The Picture of Dorian Gray*.

She also started lying at the same time, so that she'd swear, then look me straight in the eye and say it was Mummy who said it.

I had already decided that neither of my kids was learning any sense of responsibility and that they were fighting too much and eating too many candies, and in a rash of parenthood I decided to cure everything at once. I made a rule that both children were to have candy only on Monday and Friday; that each night they were to tidy up their own rooms and hang up all their clothes before seven-thirty or I would take a dime off their allowances. In an effort to forestall future fights, which I decided arose from the fact that they had no way of getting away from each other, I pronounced what I thought was my master stroke.

"If either one of you wants to play in a room by herself," I said, "all she needs to do is come and tell me."

I'm not quite sure yet why I added, "The one who *doesn't* come to me has the first choice of rooms."

The next night, hard upon a series of shrieks and crashes and the sound of dolls' heads against little girls' heads, Jane confronted me with: "Mary wants to play by herself in the bedroom, so she's going to keep kicking me until I ask you if I can play by myself, then she's going to say she wants the bedroom."

I'd already forgotten what the rule was, but I didn't want to admit my confusion, so I asked Jane how *she* would solve this little problem, pretending that I could. Her solution was that the one who came to me should have the choice of rooms. It seemed all right to me. Jane chose the living room. Then, minutes later, Mary came out and announced sweetly that she had picked up all her toys and cleaned up her room. She pointed to the clock and reminded me that Jane had just lost a dime from her allowance.

To go back on the rule was going to put me in the position of a father who showed indecision and lack of character. In a panic I said I wouldn't dock Jane, but Mary could have a candy. My wife called to me that it wasn't candy day, and Mary, in the bedroom, let go with a clearly audible, "Oh——!"

I got out of the whole thing by promising to let them both play with my typewriter the next night. It turned out to be a wonderful idea. Mary used her word on it a few times when the keys got jammed, but the psychologists were right. She finally did stop. They began to ruin my typewriter, but I figured letting them play with it would work out only to an extra expense of about twenty dollars a year in depreciation, and it gave me a chance to get my mind off the problems of being a parent and concentrate on our unsettled future and what we were going to do when we arrived back north.

Our visit to Pasadena, although out of our way, had been planned as part of our return trip to Canda; we had made our arrangements, written to our friends and family, even forwarded a deposit on an apartment in East Toronto. Even my wife, who still thought Pasadena was getting close to paradise, didn't make any serious proposal to stay. Anyway, neither of us was quite sure of what we should do. It was just that each wanted to make sure not to miss the Perfect Place to Live just for the sake of a bit of salesmanship.

10

WE TOOK the *El Capitan* from Pasadena to Chi-cago. It was a fast, direct trip that, compared to our trip west, was quiet and uneventful. After a stopover in Chicago, we arrived in Toronto with $40.37, no car, no job, no winter clothes, no house, no furniture and no idea abut where we were going to live.

We moved into the apartment. I made a last-ditch stand at being a free-lance writer and fell right in the ditch. I decided it was time to get another job.

I discovered that while I'd been looking for the Perfect Place to Live, I'd grown a lot older. Not that I'd been away long enough to make an appreciable difference; actually, it had only been about a year. It was something more than mere time. It was a frame of mind.

If I had stayed at my job and in my home town, in the normal way, I wouldn't have become so acutely conscious of what had been happening to me since my early twenties. But upsetting the relationship between myself and my environment gave me a lot of new points of view. I saw things by a kind of psychological process of triangulation.

One morning, when I was sitting in Childs' reading the employment ads, I suddenly realized with a shock that there was only one job I could apply for on the whole list. It read: "Hair Restorer Salesman, 35 to 55, with bicycle." The rest of the ads were for a lot of other people from eighteen to twenty-five, preferably with degrees in chemistry or engineering.

People whom I hadn't seen for years had turned into other people. I remember that I dropped in to see a fellow I'd gone to school with and whom I remembered as a pimply, hoop-shaped kid named Cyril Craymore, who was always trying to pry something from between his teeth with his fingernail. For some reason Cyril had always been a big joke. We used to laugh so hard at him we nearly died. In fact, the last time I'd seen him at school, he was trying to get out of a wire trash basket where he'd been stuffed by a football player named Hank Harlow, a husky, silent youngster we knew reverently as "Hinges."

Cyril was now with a paint company, and I decided to drop in on him, figuring that whatever came of it, old Cyril would be good for a laugh. When I got to him, past a couple of secretaries, I found that he had not only got loose whatever had been stuck between his teeth, but had lost his pimples, put on height and weight, especially around the shoulders, and wore a mustache and an expression as if he were still looking for Hinges.

He waved me to a seat, answered three phones, told someone to order him a taxi and somebody else to get him a lower berth away from the wheels, looked at me vaguely and said, "How's things, Harry?"

I told him Harry was another guy, and he told a girl in upswept glasses to make a note of it and asked me what I'd been doing.

I told him I'd been living in a desert writing a story about stuffing birds, and he looked as if he were making a mental note to speak to the office receptionist about who she let through the gate.

I found myself talking about such completely irrelevant subjects as the best route from Fresno to San Juan Capistrano and whether a coyote could kill a bull snake and whether it's better to live in a place with high temperatures and low humidity, or whether the human body needs a certain amount of fog. Craymore looked at me out of the corner of his eye, and I found myself in an insane conversation about the weather and unable to get off it.

In short, through a rather casual decision to find a better place to live, I'd wandered farther away from the world of

129

sales charts and gray business suits than I'd realized. I made a rather shrewd decision—to go and see if I could get my old job back, which I did.

Now that I was on salary again, I borrowed $600 for the down payment on a development house. I opened an account with the Little Love Nest Personal Help Corporation for a new houseful of furniture, another with the Signature Club for some winter clothes and signed with the Blue Horizons Automobile Finance Corporation for another secondhand car, a Hudson. Then I added up my payments and began to buy books on how to stop worrying.

I spent my lunch hours sitting with my book propped open beside a plate of fried scallops, chuckling away with Mr. Roper of Syracuse, whose stomach and insides used to twist with worry until he learned to face the worst possible thing that could happen to him. I nodded my head in agreement with the public relations and advertising director for The Ad-Idea Engineering and Sales Construction Corporation, who worried himself into a spasmodic transverse colon by not dividing his time into daytight compartments. And I resolved that the new, smooth-browed Allen would take over from now on.

But soon I'd be gnawing my nails again and thinking about my monthly payments and all that money I'd spent down there in the desert. I'd go and get another book from the library on how to turn myself into somebody else.

I don't claim that the idea of self-help isn't a good one. Doing something about human nature seems the only way out of the problems mankind gets itself into. And the human habit of worry is as good a place to start as any. But getting control of human nature is going to take some doing. If it's going to be done at all, it will probably require

130

at least as much knowledge as it took to split the atom, and it seems doubtful to me that it will be done simply by reading random thoughts on the subject by Gene Autry, Jack Dempsey, Roger Babson, Dorothy Dix and Henry Morgenthau, Jr. (who, according to one book, worried about four million four hundred thousand bushels of wheat). The advice of prominent people, although unquestionably sincere, is a bit like the advice of old gentlemen who have reached their hundredth birthday. Half will say, "I did it by leading a good clean life and never touching alcohol," and the other half will snap, "I've drunk half a cup of whisky every day since I was sixteen. It kills germs before they hit the bloodstream."

Anyway, a lot of these people offer advice that is about as applicable to the problems of the average man as advice on how to address a letter to a duke. For instance, Gene Autry said in one book, "I now get a salary of one hundred thousand a year plus one-half of all the profits on my pictures. However, I realize that this arrangement won't go on forever. But I am not worried."

Anybody who can't find anything better to worry about than losing a $100,000-a-year salary isn't a real worrier. In fact, compared to the things I worried about, just worrying about losing $100,000 a year would have amounted to refusing to face the harsh realities of life. I found myself worrying about things like who I was. I used to do this around three in the morning, when I'd wake up and lie there thinking of this and that, starting with the time I got licked by a kid named Stinky Elms and working my way up to my time-payment account. From there it would be a natural step to wondering, "Who am I?" If I fell asleep during this, I'd awaken with a loud choking "ya-a-a-k!"

and a sound of being strangled to death. As if this weren't bad enough, I took the advice of a book I'd read and tried facing the situation by imagining the worst possible thing that could happen to me.

This advice obviously originated with someone who had no imagination. I'd imagine that I kept meeting myself in different places—waiting on me at lunch counters, taking my ticket from myself at a movie. I'd imagine that I went in to see a bank manager for a loan, and when he looked up from a column of figures and said he'd love to do it, but the government wouldn't let him, it would be me. Neither of us would know what to say. We'd both give nervous little laughs, and wipe our glasses. I'd pull the bedclothes over my head.

As a matter of fact, the more books I read on how to stop worrying, the more worried I got. I worried about why the books didn't work. I worried about worry causing myopia, high blood pressure, ulcers and dental decay. I tried dividing my time into daytight compartments, and nothing happened other than a peculiar feeling around my ears as if I were being fitted for a pair of glasses. I tried watching the present moment drop like a grain of sand through an hourglass and found I could worry just as well that way as any other.

In other words, learning how to stop worrying is an admirable objective, but what cost men like Spinoza excommunication, near-martyrdom and a lifetime of study to figure out isn't going to be solved by grabbing a handful of phrases from science and philosophy and waving them like a banner in an election parade. Besides, there's another way of looking at the whole matter. We wouldn't need to learn how to stop worrying if we stopped doing the things that worry us—the sort of things I had been doing ever since I decided to look for a better life than the one I already had.

I'd wanted to do something different with my life, and I had succeeded. Now, at an age when I should have had my face turned toward the warm rays of life's afternoon, I was ankling around in the morning dew trying to collect some furniture. I not only had the things to worry about that most people worry about, I had a lot of different things of my own.

For instance, I had the unique problem of finding it hard to sit still in an office. After a year of battling around the country with the birds, I found that the prospects of staying at my desk until I was sixty-five gave me the bends, and when I should have been contemplating sales charts and surveys of housewives, I'd find myself daydreaming about all the places I hadn't seen between North Bay and Key West and a lot that I had, until I was practically ready for an oxygen tent. I was as fidgety as a sandpiper, and I established some records for getting up and walking around my desk and coming back again, for no reason at all, that still stand.

I had the feeling that I very definitely had left my search for the ideal climate unfinished. My wife and the kids and I were living in a house of our own again, but settling down is more of a mental process than a physical one, and mentally we were still living someplace else, where we intended to go as soon as we figured out where it was and how to get there. We hadn't stopped; we were out of gear, but the motor was still running.

As soon as we got in the front seat of the car, my wife and I came to life like a couple of old comedians at the smell of grease paint, one behind the wheel and the other calling out directions from a road map. We automatically got into it and went for a trip someplace every time I had a few days off. We were so obsessed with going places that a few times we even got our friends to go with us, leaving the children with a motherly old lady who used to start giving them laxatives the minute we pulled away from the door and kept it up until we got back. The children would meet us with a peculiar cross-eyed look that we couldn't figure out until we discovered this woman's system of keeping children wholesome. From then on we took the kids with us. It had become our normal way of life anyway, and the sound of tires on pavement mingling with the chatter of the kids in the back seat had taken on a domestic quality for us.

Besides, this way we were more likely to keep our friends. Often when old friends start out somewhere together in a car, laughing, talking and singing "Down by the Old Mill Stream" in four-part harmony, they arrive home with frozen little smiles, sort their bags in silence and head up their own sidewalks muttering, "Well, that's *that!*" It's well into the next oil change before they're all talking to one another again.

Ordinarily, people manage to get a measure of privacy by sulking behind closed doors, cigar smoke, woodworking lathes, petunia beds and lunches alone with a good book. But on a motor trip there's no place to hide but the trunk of the car and nothing to do but watch the peculiar way the hair comes to a point on an old friend's neck. After ten days of watching one another over bacon and eggs, beards and baggy eyes, salting tomatoes, folding road maps the wrong way, parting their hair the wrong way and staring unhappily at sausages when they distinctly ordered liver, everyone is at the breaking point, in fact well past it.

The view from Mount Holyoke, for instance, may be, as one booklet says, "an enchanting vista which will richly reward those whose steps lead them thither," but I'll always remember it as the place four of us stood around looking at a cardinal with strained little smiles, like four relatives at the reading of a will. My friend and his wife said that they had always called it a redbird and were *quite* sure a cardinal was bigger, with a green female, whereas my wife and I had always called it a cardinal, and we'd certainly *never* heard of anyone calling it a redbird north of Tennessee. It ended with us all smiling silently down at the Devil's Football, a magnetic boulder weighing 30 tons, wishing we were all home.

We all got so tired of looking at one another that we'd stand outside the motor court in the morning blinking at one another in the bright sunlight. Each of us would mutter something about going to buy some cigarettes or a pair of sunglasses or something, and we'd all walk away in opposite directions along the quiet streets, as if we'd challenged one another to duels. We'd end up spread all over town, yawning at little bronze plaques about famous battles and keep meeting one another at street corners, giving pained little laughs, chatting a moment and continuing on our ways.

All in all, taking a motor trip with friends is putting friendship to unnecessary tests. Friendship involves just one side of an adult's character. That's what makes it a friendship. A motor trip makes all sides visible at once, like when a truck runs over a beer can. I'll always remember my friend's wife, a lovely, tall brunette from Saskatchewan whom I'd always thought of as one of the most vivacious, forceful, decisive and dynamic personalities I'd ever known until I saw her standing in the middle of a motor court floor for fifteen minutes every morning, just smiling. Every morning we'd talk to her, pick up bags, rustle road maps and say briskly, "Well, 400 miles to do today! We'd better get moving," but she'd just keep smiling. It wasn't until the third morning that we discovered she was still asleep and that at home, where she usually did it in a salmon-colored housecoat, her husband just walked around her until she woke up.

Not that that kind of trait is the kind I'm talking about, but several things like that can build up tension until the whole thing ends like one of those movies of four people marooned on a mountain top, with weaknesses in character coming out all over and somebody going nuts, as I did, on that same trip. I drove through a blinding rainstorm from the famous old whaling center of Falmouth to Woods Hole, the home of the United States Bureau of Fisheries Museum and Aquarium, which hatches four million fish annually. One headlight was burned out, and I bared my teeth at the windshield and whispered, "If I wanna drive with one headlight, I'm gonna drive with one headlight!" Everybody talked to me as if they were sneaking up on me with butterfly nets. My friend's wife, in the back seat, kept saying to my wife, "Does he act like this often?" and my wife sobbed, "Yes." It all had something to do with one of the girls' wanting to pick up a pair of shoes and something washable in a blouse in Boston, when I wanted to drive another hundred miles before stopping, although how this became connected with a headlight I'm not sure.

I know that we resolved to pass up foursome motor trips with friends from then on. I realized that the gypsy life was becoming a big enough problem to us, without making things worse by losing any of our friends.

IN THE meantime there was one thing I felt sure of: it would be a lot easier to move to the Perfect Place to Live if I had a job I could take with me, and writing seemed the most feasible. I began taking a lot more interest in what I was writing at home after supper than in what I was doing at the office during the day. True to some perverse principle, now that I was in debt, confused, working in an office all day and doing my writing at night, I began to write better than I had when I had all day to do it. I began getting a few assignments from editors, and when I should have been spending my luncheons with other businessmen, beaming at after-dinner speakers over the broken bread rolls, I was out on assignments, interviewing some bum on what it was like to drink rubbing alcohol or a millionaire on how he made it.

Eventually I felt that I was getting enough assignments to quit my job and take another crack at full-time writing, and I found myself a bit dizzily working at home again, under circumstances that were the same as before in many ways, yet, at the same time, vastly different.

Mary and Jane were still traveling in spirit, in something the same way that people think they're still moving when they step onto the ground after a long train trip. They often sat in the car out in the driveway the way other kids sat in their sandboxes, the windows rolled down and their faces held up to an imaginary breeze, looking as if they were moving along at about forty-five miles an hour. At school they were confusing their teachers by reciting their allegiance to the United States of America while saluting the Union Jack, and, when asked to do a composition, writing things like "The Day the Man Pinched Me on the *El Capitan*."

But they weren't confusing the teachers any more than they were me. I was not only at home with my wife again twenty-four hours a day but a lot of the time with two other people who were changing from day to day. While my wife and I had been concentrating on finding a better climate, Mary and Jane had changed from toddlers to two little people, a lot shorter than we were, but equipped with full-sized wills, egos and ideas of their own. Mary was now showing definite indications of becoming a carpenter and was moving around fast trying to make things like TV sets out of old orange crates. Jane was showing signs of becoming a philosopher—one with a directly opposite philosophy on everything than the one I had—and was prepared to defend her position with pigtails flying.

Both of them had stopped saying, "That's my Daddy," with the small child's pride and reverence and had started saying, "That's my Daddy," in a tone that implied, "But we didn't have anything to do with choosing him." They began comparing me with their schoolteachers and wondering how I'd got by so long, until I was doodling on the margins of my manuscript paper, drawing funny faces, writing "TEACHER" under them and mentally throwing spitballs and putting thumbtacks on chairs. One teacher in particular, a big, gangling, six-foot farmer's son named Wire, evidently used to sit in the schoolroom doing the same thing to me and dreaming up things to drive me nuts.

One favorite trick of his was to wait till Mary appeared at school wearing a new dress then think up what he called a "project." This consisted of making little model farms, with cows and everything, out of a mixture he made himself out of melted crayons, chalk, berry juice and mucilage. Mary would come in the door stained from head to foot under the auspices of the whole educational system and say casually, "Mr. Wire gave us a project today."

My wife would take one look at her, turn to me and tell

me that I could fork over five dollars for a new dress. She knew from experience that this stuff Wire whipped up was a permanent dye that dug in like a tattoo. My wife tried everything on it, including nail-polish remover, and it wouldn't move. One lunch hour, after one of these projects, I saw three mothers all come out onto their porches, holding up frocks to one another, then all turn like pioneer mothers looking toward Pawnee country and look toward the school, where Wire was sitting dreaming up the next day's project.

"We're going to make colored birds out of pieces of soap tomorrow," Mary would say happily. "Mr. Wire said to ask you for some fountain pen ink, cocoa, a can of number twenty motor oil and your electric razor."

I began to visualize Wire sitting at his desk, while his class scratched away busily, dozing over some book called *Adventures in Punctuation* and thinking up new ways to irritate me.

Sometimes he did it with casual little remarks. Mary wouldn't believe anything I told her, but Wire could have told her that the sun was four inches wide and made out of old light bulbs and she would have included it among the facts of nature. I didn't mind it when he stuck to remarks about schoolwork, but sometimes he evidently just said anything that came into his head. One time he told Mary that little girls should never sleep in after six in the morning, as it was bad for their spines. The result was that I had her up at about five thirty getting in my way while I tried to make my breakfast and asking me things like how you go about getting pregnant before I'd even had my coffee.

One time he arranged for me to take charge of six kids

at a school outing to a pioneer museum in a town twenty miles away. He made each parent responsible for each group's turning in a report, with the result that before the day was over, I was walking on my ankles trying to get the answers to: (a) name eight instruments used by black-smiths; (b) tell how the early settlers delivered mail; (c) draw a diagram of the museum; (d) name six countries where you find owls. That night the outing was followed by a school concert. I saw Wire, grinning at me and eating my wife's fudge, sitting behind a fat, scowling little boy who was blowing a trumpet.

The kids thought everything Wire said was funny. His humor, as relayed to me at the supper table, left me helping myself to more creamed peas, but the kids thought he was a riot.

"Gee Mr. Wire was funny today," Mary would say. "He's the *craziest* man. Today he said—" her voice would go taut and wavering with mirth—"he said, 'I'm thirsty,' and went to the fountain and had a drink of water. Honest, the whole class nearly rolled on the floor."

I'd wait to hear what Wire said when he lifted his head from the fountain. Maybe he'd let the water drip from his chin, pretended he was a buffalo surprised at a water hole and stomped up and down the aisles. But my kid would just start helping herself to more potatoes. Evidently the joke was over. What Wire did that put the kids in the aisles was to say he was thirsty. This guy must have got his gags out of a seed catalogue, but he sure panicked the kids.

Wire evidently worked in cahoots with a Miss Ogilvie, who was Jane's home economics teacher. For the past year we'd been trying to get Jane to take some interest in the house, and she still thought she was being persecuted if we told her to pick her socks up off the floor. But after five days of home economics, Ogilvie and Wire had her asking us for materials to make a cake that cost half my wife's allowance.

"Miss Ogilvie said that she'd only use six eggs to show us how," Jane would explain, "but at home people always use two dozen."

Ogilvie was evidently about as practical a gal as a niece of mine who ran off with Ringling Brothers and Barnum and Bailey to be a sword swallower.

"Miss Ogilvie says tonight we are to help our mothers stuff a pheasant with English chestnuts and zinfandel sauce," Jane would say to her mother. "Where do you keep them?"

The maddening part of all this, of course, was that my kids doted on their teachers, and their teachers knew it, and I had the conviction that it filled Wire, particularly, with glee while he sat in his classroom giving me the slow burn.

One sunny spring morning I came downstairs feeling especially good, tossed off my tomato juice and said to Mary, "Well, waddaya say we play hookey today?"

"Play what?" she asked.

"Play hookey," I said. "We can smoke stinkworts and spear frogs."

She looked at her mother and back to me as if I'd gone nuts. "What's it mean?" she said.

"What's it *mean?*" I yelped. I turned to my wife. "Look, f'r—what are they teaching kids today, when they don't even know what playing hookey means?" I turned back to my kid. "It means staying away from school."

143

Mary was getting more and more baffled. "Why should I stay away from school?"

I was beginning to feel irresponsible, an unfit father for a well-adjusted child, and a bit like an old juvenile delinquent.

"You mean you don't want to stay away from school?" I asked.

"Why should I stay away from school? Today we have a movie, play tennis, correct our teacher's mistakes, have phys ed, home ec, group co-operation and square dancing, play basketball and write a report for Mr. Wire on what we don't like about parents."

I began to feel exactly the way I used to feel when I was a kid on the way to the principal's office to get strapped, peered at by clean, neat little girls in middies who took a couple of steps sideways to let me pass.

In fact, I ran up against something that it seemed to me had not received enough attention from child psychology. Parents, I'd been led to believe, were responsible for their children's becoming tense, anxious, criminal, shy, retarded and withdrawn, and I'd been on the lookout for any signs of maladjustment. Now I began to find that children could cause all those things to happen to parents, do it faster and have more fun at it.

I found that one of the commonest forms of maladjustment a child can cause is a tendency in the parents to withdraw from each other—not because of any lessening of their affection, but because they never hear from each other any more.

My wife and I had made up our minds early that our children were going to express themselves as freely as a barber before a holiday week end. Mealtimes were going

144

to be occasions for mutual and lively exchange of ideas. Now that I was at home for most of my meals, and the children were beginning to move around in their own world, my wife and I found ourselves sitting there looking from one kid to the other like spectators at a tennis match. We withheld vital communiqués about the state of our coalbin and how we were going to pay the Homemaker's Friend Little Loan Corporation while we listened to a never-ending cross fire of conversation about skipping ropes, cats, orange crates and the adventures of comic-book characters. The kids stopped to breathe only between paragraphs, in quick, sucking gasps, and the only way my wife and I could get a remark in was to run in the way little girls do in double Dutch. It began to stunt our development.

It dawned on us that kids will never stop talking unless someone stops them. In desperation I'd say, "Nobody's to say another word until we've reached dessert," and threaten to penalize the first offender by taking a nickel off her allowance, one of the things that would impress both my daughters, who were so tight it was embarrassing. The silence would come on us so suddenly that neither my wife nor I would be able to think of anything to say.

We began to find that if any molding of character is going to be done, it's going to be done to somebody over thirty-five, not under ten. For one thing, my wife and I were so full of self-doubts we were ready to be molded into anything, whereas the kids' opinions about everything had set like cement. We faced the children with old, leaky nervous systems held together by Scotch tape. The kids, on the other hand, spearheaded nature's greatest molding force, the law of survival, with baby buggies, roller skates and systems of brand-new nerves like baling wire.

A child has more time to influence parents than parents have to influence children and can do it with any household object. One week I watched Jane, with just a navy blue sweater, mold my wife's character until she was breaking out in blotches. When my wife insisted that she wear it to school, Jane would try to wear it without putting it on. She'd wander sullenly to school, wearing the sweater as if it were someone else's stole. She'd put an arm in one sleeve and let the other dangle, wear it in a peculiar way so that it looked as if it wasn't with her, stretch it, leave it on buses and in lockers and drop it down manholes. She could have kept it up until she was eighty, and she molded her mother into a shape where her mother was seeing her off to school every morning with some remark like, "If you get pneumonia and die, don't come to me about it." Then she'd close the door, light a cigarette and take a drag that lasted almost till the second school bell.

I was determined to play ball with the child psychologists by never belting my kids. At the same time, I realized that discipline was absolutely necessary, and I was compromising by just trying to *look* as if I were going to belt them. It was like pretending I was breathing. I've put so much energy behind some of my fierce expressions that I've nearly popped my glasses off my nose with sheer blood pressure, and it left me bristling with repressions like an old hound with sandspurs. I developed more tics than the kids, including one of suddenly arching my back as if someone had dropped an ice cube down my collar and sniffing so that the cords on my neck tightened like piano wires.

Another thing, all my ideas about children were based on recollections of my own boyhood. I learned that this was a mistake—little girls are different from little boys.

For one thing, clothes to a girl touch some deep, instinctive emotional spring that is formed, I think, with her first pink booties. My daughters started thumping around on their heels, their pigtails sticking out like rockets, accusing my wife of trying to sabotage their charm.

"You want me to wear that HORRIBLE brown skirt with that DISGUSTING blouse and that LOATHESOME wide belt because you HATE me and you want me to look AWFUL, because you think it's FUNNY to see people LAUGH at me," they'd say, convinced that the whole thing was a plot based on jealousy. They wanted to go to school dressed like glamorous young movie stars and spent most of their time standing in front of their bedroom mirrors, which were decorated with characters from *Peter Rabbit*, trying on brassieres made out of knotted handkerchiefs filled with bolts, building blocks and doll stuffing, to see how they'd look.

I was now also getting thoroughly involved in the problem of children's allowances and wishing that child psychologists would get onto some other subject. Every time I read what the latest expert had to say on the subject, it cost me more dough. Not only that, it began to teach my kids a lot of bad habits.

I read in an article by a child psychologist that the purpose of an allowance is to teach children to handle money. I gave them twenty-five cents more a week and told them that either they paid for their own movies when we went on Friday nights or went without. Both of my kids loved movies. So did I.

The first week Mary didn't have any money left to pay for hers.

"Aha!" I said, thinking that at last I'd found something

that would make an impression. "You see what money means? Now you can't go to a movie tonight."

The thought suddenly dawned on me that neither could I—unless I paid two bucks for a sitter.

"Okay," I snapped, "let that be a lesson to you. Tonight I'll loan you a quarter, but it will come off your allowance next week."

This taught her how to borrow. She borrowed two-bits again next week, because she didn't have any money left. This time she smiled. Pretty soon she owed me $9.75. Not only that, she was the only kid on the block not getting an allowance. She began to develop tics. I started lending her her whole allowance.

So I decided, well, by gosh, I'll make them pay for something they go to *without* me. I gave them another quarter more a week and told them that they would have to pay their own Sunday-school collection. They both stopped going to Sunday school. They made another quarter a week this way, bringing the total up to $1.50. They got it Saturday morning, spent it Saturday afternoon and sat back waiting for the next pension.

They were now getting fifty cents a week more out of me than they were when I had no idea what an allowance was for.

But I was sure the psychologists must be right, somehow. I told them that from now on they would have to buy all gifts out of their own allowance and gave them another quarter a week, bringing the take up to $1.75. They stopped giving me presents. They just cut off Christmas, Father's Day and my birthday. I couldn't ask them where my present was, or it would have been teaching them to be greedy, and they knew it.

In fact, nothing seemed to work. The kids were now getting so much money every week that I was borrowing from them. They spent it on two things—*Klassix Komix* and *Komix Klassix*. When they were buying ten comic books a week, I put my foot down. I told them that they could only buy one and thought that would fix things so I could get into their rooms without skating on two inches of comic books. They found a *Giant Comic Book* for $1.75.

I told them that they couldn't buy *any* comic books. But I remembered what the psychologists said. The idea was to teach them how to shop. I told them they could buy anything else. Mary came home with an egg slicer, a little bird cage, a jug, three skipping ropes, a bottle of nail polish and some glue for insoles. Jane came home with seven movie magazines and the confessions of a marijuana smoker.

In the meantime they knew that anything important that turned up, I would pay for. The last time I decided that I wouldn't take them to anything that they couldn't afford themselves was the week a kids' movie that had been advertised for six months and was recommended by their schoolteachers, came to town, and they were invited to three birthday parties, a Girl Scout rally and a school picnic. By the time they'd told everyone their father wouldn't let them go to anything, the principal, two teachers, three mothers and a Brown Owl had stopped speaking to me, and the kids just sat around chewing bubble gum and waiting for me to crack, which I did, of course. I cracked so completely that I forgot the whole principle of children's allowances, stopped reading books by experts on the subject and just gave them their money every week and forgot about it.

While I was coping with my kids, I was also coping with neighbors. I'd learned a lot about neighbors while moving around looking for the right place to live. I'd had plenty. In the past year I'd lived beside a professor of astronomy, an electric-guitar player, a cowboy, a bank manager, a professional contest enterer with a 1923 Rolls-Royce and long hair, and a lot of people with short hair and Fords who were sometimes the strangest of them all. And I'd got along fine, but I'd learned a few tricks.

One thing I'd learned was that there is a certain safety measure in addressing a neighbor as "mister." This often made me look like a stuffed shirt, but I'd found that little conventions like that keep the seams all nice and snug. You never hear anyone say, "If there's one guy I'd like to clobber, it's that Mr. Anderson." It's only when you can call a guy George that you can really get homicidal.

I saw it work out in my new home, which was in a brand-new district north of Toronto with a lot of new people. I lived beside a tall, casual young calculating-machine salesman with two small children and a slow boyish grin, and when I called him "mister" the first night, he said, "Look, just call me Harry. I'm just an ordinary guy. How about dropping over for a beer when you get the stove connected? Where do you get that "mister" stuff?"

Where I got it was moving in beside guys who asked me to call them Harry, and he was no exception. He gripped my hand as I came up the walk just ahead of the furniture movers, asked my wife's name, put a brotherly arm around her and said, "Okay, Helen, you and Irma just make yourselves comfortable out by our barbeque while Bob and I whip up some roast wieners." He asked my wife if she'd mind bringing a wiener fork, as they'd lost theirs, put on a chef's cap with "Dig In" lettered on it, and stopped speaking to me for a year and a half.

He didn't stop speaking to me that night, of course. It was the next night. He liked to park his car in our mutual driveway. Each time I wanted in or out of my garage, I had to work my way between two ornamental bushes of thorns, knock at his door, get him off his couch and explain to him that I had to go to the store for some curtain rings. He'd whip his car out like a parking-lot attendant, let mine out, park in the middle of the driveway again and go in the house, obviously thinking, "I give this guy a big welcome with wieners; now he's trying to make it tough for me to own a car."

Every time he came to the door in his slippers and a dressing gown, he was a bit more distant, until he was finally looking at me as if I were selling enlargements for baby pictures. This expression he held, as I say, for a year and a half, except once when he leaned on our gate and said distantly, "Here's your wiener fork," and another time, the following spring, when he looked haughtily over the top of my hat and asked me if I'd mind having my children clean some firecrackers off his lawn.

There's a strange bit of psychology at work when you call someone "mister." When you call a person "mister," you have a mild and pleasant desire to get to know him better. If you keep it in check, it's a sound relationship and can go on for years. But once you start calling someone by his first name, the next interesting step is to get sore at him.

Another dangerous practice, I'd found, was just dropping in on neighbors for a few minutes unannounced. A lot of things can happen in a few minutes, and they often happen when someone drops in. One man across the road used to drop in on me in the morning on his days off. It was during

151

a period when I was trying a new scheme to quit smoking without giving up cigarettes. I'd arrived at a system of putting off my first cigarette and morning coffee until ten thirty. I was fine if no one spoke to me or touched me and I didn't have to move around too much. My family simply avoided me.

This guy, who had hips wider than his shoulders, was hard enough to take even when you were smoking and leaning on a hoe. He talked in ellipses. If you said, "It's a nice day," he'd say something like, "It can't all the time," and look at you through a crack between his glasses and his nose as if you shared some mystery, which indeed you did. If you saw him coming home in the daytime and said, "You on night shift now?" he'd look at you knowingly and answer something like, "Buses don't run for nothing," and give a high, leafy laugh.

If you said you thought there was something wrong with the rear end of your car, he'd look at you and say solemnly, "Give me your keys."

You'd look at him in surprise.

"*Give—me—your—keys,*" he'd repeat patiently, his tone implying that he had been in charge of tuning up motors for the Underground during the war, or was at least an incognito squad-car mechanic from Scotland Yard.

Actually he sold lamps, but the point is I'll never forget those mad, midmorning conversations as long as I live, with him talking in spirals, bursting out into hysterical laughter, and me trying to see him without cigarettes, trying to remember his name and track down his remarks.

Another thing I'd learned was to watch what I said to new neighbors until I was sure what they were like—something particularly important if the talk leads to anything in the nature of enthusiasms or confidences. I remember one time I forgot this. I told one neighbor and his straight-forward wife the first time I was talking to them that I loved the ballet, Jelly Roll Morton, very light beer, Johnny Walker's Black Label, Schopenhauer, Mexican cigarettes, Mugsy Spanier, old alley cats, Jane Russell, prize fights and I'd like to try marijuana someday. I noticed them both looking at me as if they'd seen a flying saucer. I found later that they both belonged to something called the Seven-Square Way of Life, based on the seven points of complete disapproval of smoking, drinking, dancing, movies, laughing, reading and love.

I'd learned, too, never to go by first impressions of my neighbors. One of my very best neighbors was a powerful red-haired woman named Muskeg Mary who everybody in the block warned me was the district drunk and its most determined sinner, and who turned out to be one of the most genuinely Christian people I've ever met. If I got stuck in a drift in my driveway at three in the morning at thirty below, Mary would appear, cursing and chuckling juicily, her curlers gleaming in the moonlight, and nearly lift my car up onto her shoulders. She was always on the job when I needed a friend, and we still exchange Christmas cards. She presses leaves and things in hers.

12

WHEN you are convinced that somehow you are going to end up in the perfect place, you unconsciously assume that any place you happen to be in is a temporary stopover, even if you happen to have put a down payment on it. We had never really settled down in our new house. I'd bought it only because I figured buying would be more economical than renting while we made new plans for future bliss. Mentally we were still living in some other place.

But in some subtle but important way, our outlook had changed, until our objective was no longer a simple intention to move to a place with a perfect climate, but just to move. Without actually being aware of it, we were convinced that moving could solve just about everything, from the common cold to even more common boredom. It was in keeping with the restlessness which was now the keynote of our lives that when my wife and I had one of those main-event fights that all marriages seem to have to go through, instead of deciding to go to a marriage counselor, we just decided to move, this time to a farm.

It was a time when marriage counselors first began to appear regularly in the periodicals. At least half the magazines you picked up had a feature article starting off with one of those phony conversations that take place between a woman named Mrs. X and a counselor who leans back, smiles mysteriously, makes a tent of his fingers and says, "What makes you think your husband doesn't love you, just because he chased you around the house with an ax?"

Mrs. X looks up, surprised, and says, "You mean, then, Doctor, that both of us are focusing our emotions on a pre-formulated aspect of the husband-wife relationship, and that this is just a normal adjustment of our personality patterns?"

"Exactly," smiles the doctor.

He then tells her about the five phases of love and how

she must give a lot of thought and attention to making marriage work.

It was one of these articles that caused this fight my wife and I had, or at least made it such a spectacular one. We had always had the normal, healthy number of flare-ups, without their developing into major conflagrations. But my wife either started taking seriously these articles on how to bring harmony into the home, or she discovered they provided a wonderful new technique for driving me mad. She began meeting my outbursts with a calm, well-informed smile. I started to do everything but sneak up and cut the ends off her permanent and yell, "My old man can lick your old man," to get her to fight. But all she'd do would be to look like a lady psychiatrist and say, "Don't you think, dear, we could talk it over more sensibly in the morning?"

I didn't want to talk it over in the morning. I wanted to kick her around right away. To be left dangling alone on the end of a bad mood left me feeling like an overtrained zombie and behaving like one, until my wife suddenly rolled up the latest magazine carrying an article on "How to Make Marriage Work" and threw it at me, missing me by a foot but making me move so fast that I jarred my glasses sideways.

It was a Saturday morning, and we were both half awake and hadn't had our coffee yet. We were soon walking around not noticing what we were doing, putting sugar in the coffee percolator, pouring cream in the sugar bowl and taking deep swallows from coffee cups that we'd forgotten to put coffee in. We got rid of great gobs of frustration by pointing fingers at each other and saying things like, "I HAVE JUST ABOUT REACHED THE END OF MY

TETHER." We stood at open doors taking deep breaths of air, came back into the house and thumbed through the yellow pages of the phone book looking for the numbers of hotels, divorce lawyers and old girl friends, and, in our excited state, looked for all of them under headings like Used-Car Parts. The kids stood beside their mother, making a little tableau like an early pioneer family waiting to be scalped.

When we'd finished, we felt a fine healthy glow, as if we'd had a cold shower and a rubdown, and sat around going over with delight the things we'd said to each other.

"Well, I never realized that you'd given up a burning ambition to be the world's greatest mountain climber just to marry me," my wife said, making a new batch of coffee.

"So your best friends told you never to trust a man with my kind of ears, did they?" I said, closing my eyes and taking a bit of toast and marmalade.

But the thing is, it all started us taking stock of things— our lives, the past few years, our future. For us it was a logical step to start talking about moving again and trying someplace else, with more space around us.

Ever since I had first got the notion of being a writer, able to live where and how I pleased, one of the pictures I'd carried around in the back of my head was one of me with one foot on a rail fence, chewing a piece of timothy and looking into the sunset, a real mystic of nature; or sitting in a country garden with my writing pad on my knee, looking a bit like a picture I'd once seen of John Galsworthy.

Now that I was an independent writer again, I realized that I really could live on a farm. My wife and I decided that life in the country, although it wouldn't solve the problem of the weather in one way, might solve it in another. We'd be closer to nature, and if there was snow, it at least would be clean and unsullied. We'd be free of the rush and traffic jams that made winter in the city something we felt everyone should move away from if possible. Anyway, it would be a nice way to live while we made up our minds just where the Perfect Place to Live was located.

This time we knew all the tricks of selling a house, including dropping the price at the beginning instead of later on, and we closed the deal with a kindly-looking old gentleman with pink skin and snow-white hair and merry, honest blue eyes. He tried to chisel me out of everything I owned, claiming that it was attached to the house, even if he found it just leaning against it. For a while there I thought he had his eye on my wife.

My wife and I had to sign some papers at the bank before the actual money for the house was handed over, and we met my lawyer there. We all stood at the counter happily handing papers back and forth to one another. My favorite teller beamed on me from behind his bars, figuring that I must have made the grade at last with all this money changing hands, and when it was all over, I found myself with a smile stuck sideways on my face as I looked at an old envelope on which I'd made some last-minute calculations. I realized that by the time I'd cleared up a few extra mortgages I'd raised and got myself somewhere near solvency, if I were going to keep enough capital intact to bail me out of the country if necessary, I'd have to write and sell something before we reached our new home.

I had lined up a farm to rent near Elmvale, Ontario, and one mellow, lazy fall afternoon, an hour after a van had left carrying our furniture, I let out the clutch and the car started down the driveway.

By now we were so accustomed to rolling away from empty houses that nobody looked up until I made a slight attempt to whip up the old spirit of adventure. I waved out the window without looking and called:

"Good-by, house!"

At the sound, Mary looked up from her comic book, sniffed thoughtfully and said without expression, "Good-by, driveway."

Jane just waved her hand without looking up from her movie magazine, finished the paragraph she'd been reading then looked up and said, "Good-by, lawn."

"Good-by," my wife said, as if aroused from thoughts of a lot of other things. She looked with a faint smile from one to the other of us. We all grinned a bit wearily and went back to comic book, movie magazine, private thoughts and steering.

Jane and Mary started going to a one-room country school called S.S. No. 12, Tiny Township, a mellowed old rectangle attached to a woodshed and pleasantly cluttered inside with charts, prints, cutouts, pussy willows, bird lists, pots of sprouting oats and kids' drawings. It was attended by nine children, from seven to fourteen, and was presided over by a cheerful, kindly, stouthearted woman who took the part of a combined schoolmarm, scout leader and favorite aunt. The pupils were all farmers' children, polite, a bit shy and, of course, involved in the rural world of their parents. Into this world they courteously accepted Mary and Jane, who now, as well as having a basic knowledge of the Constitution of the United States, became experts in

159

the care of Canadian Holsteins. Mary also struck up an abiding friendship with the farmer who rented the land and became quite a hand at driving a tractor. As soon as she got home from school, he moved over and let her take over at the wheel, and from then until suppertime they passed our side door at regular intervals on the other side of a cedar hedge, just their heads and shoulders visible in a cloud of dust as Mary churned up the east forty.

The farmer also plowed up our gardens for us from virgin turf and was so pleased at the sight of city folk actually trying to do something useful that every time he had a load of spare manure, he hauled it over and dumped it on our vegetable garden. As a result we had what was probably the most active vegetable garden in the county. I've never seen such a crop of vegetables and flowers before or since. We had sunflowers eleven feet high, by actual measurement, and the pumpkin and squash vines grew so fast in all directions from the garden that every time I walked past them, I instinctively stepped lively, half-expecting them to throw a loop around me.

This farm was without a doubt one of the most charming spots I've ever seen. There was only one thing wrong with it from the point of view of city people—it was too far from the city. We did what all city people do when they go to farms to live: we tried to bring the city to the country. We had city friends for the week end, and other city friends who lived on farms in other parts of the country had us to their farms for week ends, until I finally quit and began spending my week ends sitting behind the silo looking at the steers.

When on a trip to the city I ran into some enthusiast who said, "Look, we'll have to arrange a week end in the country. We've bought an old farm, you know. Not a *real* farm. I mean, we haven't any cows. But it's an old farmhouse we've fixed up. Wait till you see it," I said, "Sounds fun," or "I'll call you someday." Sometimes I used an invention of my own made up of them both: "Sounds funny call someday," and slipped off into the crowd, nodding and waving.

In the first place, the fact that someone has slip-covered the old silo in chintz, equipped the root cellar with bunks, decorated the old pantry with sketches of lobsters and Martini glasses, kicked out the partition between the parlor and the summer kitchen and changed the whole thing from R.R. No. 3 to "The Button Hook," or "The Snuggery," doesn't alter the fact that one of these renovated farms is someone else's home. Nor do a lot of maps with cartoons showing how to find it ("Turn right at the church, go a quarter of a mile to the first dirt road, follow to old general store, now a filling station, past the cemetery to the big fallen-down gate. That's us. Just remember, as long as you're on pavement you're not there.") alter the fact that a week end with six strangers is just a party that reaches that blank spot where everyone says "Twenty past eight!" and laughs, then keeps right on going for another thirty-six hours.

I've known only one man who could be gay company for thirty-six hours. He was a third earl with an Oxford accent, frayed cuffs and a terrific gift of conversation, but even he started priming himself with his toothbrush water and kept it up all day, until around eleven o'clock at night he was standing down by the old pond, lecturing the frogs on the overtones of a fugue.

Anyone else I know at the end of the first day of concentrated companionship looks as if he'd just sat through a double feature including *Gone with the Wind* and *From Here to Eternity* and ten "Porky Pig" cartoons. It ends up with everyone sitting on his spine with his neck bent against the wall, listening to one determined guest play a little ineffectual Chopin and a little awful *Oklahoma!* on a damp piano and wondering desperately what is the first decent moment he can leave.

Perhaps I need more solitude than most people. I know around eleven o'clock on Sunday morning of a social week end at our place, I would find myself slipping into old barns and tool sheds and crouching behind fences like a rabbit, startling guests who came upon me in unlikely places. My wife used to locate me not by looking for the gayest group of guests but by peering over the fields watching for the flight of startled plovers.

I know some of our guests, at least, felt the same as I did about two days of unbroken conviviality. I remember one man with thin wavy hair and close-set eyes who was brought along by a friend of mine and introduced as a friend from Moncton. We forgot each other's names as soon as we were introduced, although I associate him vaguely with life insurance, but we kept coming across each other in out-of-the-way places where we'd gone to sulk—in the middle of thickets or sitting with our elbows on our knees, trying to hit ants by dropping little pieces of straw from our teeth. Once I crawled like a raccoon into a broken-down shed and, after my eyes got accustomed to the gloom, found this man sitting in an old buggy, one arm on the back of the seat, smiling imperiously at what I'm sure were cheering crowds. He nodded bleakly at me, said, "These buggies were really

162

comfortable," got up without another word and left through a door used for hay.

In fact this was a week end that contributed to our final decision to go back to the city. I'd met a commercial artist who had just come back from England and who wanted to have a big reunion with a lot of his friends. But he and his wife were living in a small flat in Toronto, and in an insane moment I suggested that he hold a week-end party at my farm. He jumped at the chance. He and his wife began phoning some of the strangest characters I've ever met, some of whom brought their relatives. There was a tall, hysterical supervisor of a window-display department, who told me that he could never go to sleep, literally, unless there was a hole at both ends of the bed sheet—not just one for his head, but one at the other end. If a bed was tucked in at the foot, he said, he almost suffocated. I also learned that he read a book on the history of Greek philosophy the size of an encyclopedia every night, peering at it till his eyes crossed and he fell into a swoon. He had been reading it for a year and was still on page ten.

There were a ponderous, dark, slow-spoken Irishman with a wide face, who always got ill at the sight of roast lamb (although nobody knew this at first) and a tall, thin young man with a mustache and a duodenal ulcer. His plump, busy wife explained earnestly, in a tone that she hoped wouldn't hurt anyone's feelings, "George never eats fat or white bread, no tomatoes and nothing leguminous," while George sat there smiling as if he'd accomplished something.

There was also a dog, a successful girl portrait-painter, somebody's mother, who asked anxiously if many trains

163

passed along the tracks at the foot of the property, and the man with the Oxford accent I mentioned earlier.

Right after the dog sent six farm cats flying for the trees, I raced around ahead of everyone, acquainting them with the house. I dwelt at length on the plumbing system. As far as I had been able to figure out, the well was fed by a buried glacial spring that was just about finished. The well had gone dry, in fact, the day before but was filling up at the rate of an inch an hour. If you had a bath, it ran dry. If you let the water run till it was cold, it ran dry. If you flushed the toilet, it ran dry, although the septic tank overflowed.

I explained—with laughing interjections about "We're right out in the country, you know"—that the taps with the white handles were drinking water, except in the bathroom, where the drinking water was the tap in the bathtub. I told them not to drink from the taps without white handles.

At least I thought that was what I said. The man with the ulcer told me afterward that he thought I said not to drink from the taps with white handles except in the bathtub.

I don't know whether you actually get high on cistern water, but that night, before dinner, this man was so witty and vivacious that my wife asked him gaily if he'd mind helping with the drinks. Everyone took Scotch and water—cistern water. This guy cleverly avoided all the taps with white handles.

We gathered for a dinner of roast lamb, and the Irishman took one look at the table and hesitated in the doorway like a well-brought-up young lady looking for the guest of honor. Just then the man who had mixed the drinks said,

164

"By golly! That well water is wonderful. Full of sulphur and minerals. Faint taste of peanuts, too."

My wife and I looked at each other and turned pale—as pale as only city people who have looked into a cistern can get.

It was only the beginning of a lot of things that happened that week end. The last thing I remember doing before darkness settled on the house was skipping nervously around outside the bathroom, where the portrait-painter had just disappeared, biting my nails till I finally got up the nerve to say, "If you don't hold the handle down a sec, it will overflow."

Nothing quite reached a climax that night, although it sounded a few times as if it were going to. We heard the dog whining in the kitchen, at which the Oxford man, who had been helped to bed, boomed out a line from Coleridge: "What ails the mastiff bitch?" Then I went to sleep, until the train passed the house. This was a sound that I still wasn't used to myself, and I leaped out of bed thinking it was an earthquake. I was passed in the hall by the little old lady, who had cotton batting in both her ears. I don't know where she was going, but I suspect it was to try to catch a bus back to the city.

A little later there was another commotion from the window dresser's room. It turned out that his wife, awaking half-frozen, had decided, for once, to hell with her husband and had not only tucked the bed sheets in at the foot of the bed but had put both their coats over them. He had awakened later, in a pitch-black country bedroom, thinking that he was suffocating, screamed that he was dying, jumped out of bed and tripped over his Greek philosophy.

165

There was no more beautiful sight than the sun coming up that morning. I met the Irishman on the stairs. He said he'd have to go home around noon. I think most of us secretly agreed with the Irishman. City people should have week ends in the city, and country people should have week ends in the country.

IN between week ends what I found myself doing most of the time was fighting with wild animals, often in my pajamas and armed only with a broom, with my wife, white-faced and loyal, standing behind me with a rock, in case I missed.

Something overlooked by most people, who think it's only necessary to get away from a time clock to become part of a pastoral idyl, is that outside the city millions of things are champing their teeth, rubbing their paws, filling scent bags, waving feelers, mooing, neighing, pawing, stomping, whimpering, screeching, gibbering, gnawing through woodwork and running under woodwork.

This will come as no surprise to people born in the country. It did to me. I was born within the sound of malted-milk machines and the snick of traffic lights. At that I probably would have adapted myself if I hadn't been trying to combine the country sounds with a city life. I was trying to live in the country with my supply lines deep in the city. At times it was a lot like repairing a transmission line in a starched shirt.

For instance, once I had a showdown with a skunk at ten in the morning. To a farmer or a prospector or an explorer, this would have been all in the day's work. He would have spent the rest of the day far from his fellow man, out in the fields or deep in the woods, getting deodorized by the sun and wind. But three hours later I was having lunch with the editor of a woman's magazine that chiefly advertises expensive perfume. She kept looking at my suit and secretly smelling the soup and French bread. I kept talking fast, telling jokes and laughing at them, smoking cigarettes continually and ignoring her puzzled little frown when I tried to talk her into having a cigarette with her soup and ice cream. That sort of thing can make you look mighty strange.

It had all started when I discovered I had a skunk under

168

the farmhouse porch. I let the thing alone, sentimentally believing that if you leave them alone, they'll leave you alone. Then one night several things happened at once. At 4:30 A.M., while sleeping on the porch under the stars, I awoke to find myself being strafed by bats that lived in the eaves right over my head, and at the same time I realized that my skunk was having a fight with something under the floor. I don't know who won. I know that if it wasn't my skunk, it was a hollow victory for the other animal.

I bolted for indoors, startling the bats, who emitted tiny screams, which made me emit tiny screams, and helped my wife, who was racing around closing windows. Later, as I went around spraying the rooms with cologne, I decided the friendship between me and the skunk was an impossible one. The next morning I built a box trap from a diagram I found in an old boy scout guide, determined to cart the skunk off and turn him loose in a forest. An old timer told me, "Won't do a thing as long as you handle him nice and gentle."

I set the trap and forgot about it, with a city boy's conviction that traps only worked in adventure stories. I heard the lid clunk down at nine-thirty in the morning, just as I was having a last cup of coffee before setting off for the city with a manuscript. I couldn't leave my wife there with a live skunk in a box—I was already leaving her without any housekeeping allowance. I put the box in the trunk of the car and started off as if I were carrying the crown jewels, intending to stop at a little grove about a half a mile away, where I figured I'd like to live if I were a skunk.

When I reached the grove, I gently took the trap out of the trunk and put it in the grass, and, while a blue jay and a squirrel looked on, gently pulled the lid back by a long

169

cord. The skunk stayed in the box. I took a branch and tapped the end. Nothing happened. I got a bit impatient and gave the box a kick, running away at the same time. My pants caught in some brambles, and I staggered and fell onto my hands and knees, cracking several dead branches and sounding so much like a charging grizzly that the blue jay screamed and the squirrel shot around the tree chattering hysterically. I got up, but not fast enough. The skunk had come out this time. The last I saw of him, he was heading slowly for a stump, looking alive and well, but it must have taken him a year or so to get recharged. Incidentally, I sold the manuscript. I've never seen an editor make such a quick decision in my life.

During my life in the country, I fought to hold my own against chipmunks, black squirrels, red squirrels, weasels, raccoons, robins and things I never saw but which often squeaked at three in the morning. Sometimes I thought I was winning; sometimes I knew I was slowly being driven back to the city.

When I'd taken the farm, the idea of getting back to the good old days of good old wood stoves, good old summer kitchens, good old well water and the good old pioneer life in general had appealed to me. I discovered that all those quaint little elm-arched streets you drive through on a holiday week end are where all the good old rats live before they get muscled out by the healthiest ones and try to make a go of it in the city. They come into farmhouses, village shops, barns and under verandas in the fall, and if they like it, they invite their relatives.

A real farmer, I suppose, just nails these things with a pitchfork and goes on forking hay. I'd never used a pitchfork in my life, having spent most of my life in the advertising business, where we used pencils. The first rat I saw was in our cistern cellar, which looked like a cross between an early Lon Chaney movie set and a scene on a poster on how to prevent malaria. When I had to go into the place, I'd kick the door open and stand back like a private detective breaking in on a mob. And when I was in the tub having a bath, lying back in the steaming yellow rain water, amid little twigs and old leaves, I couldn't enjoy it for thinking where the water came from. This time, when I saw a rat, I staggered upstairs, pale and popeyed, told my wife to stand guard over the children and staggered over to a neighboring farmer's for advice. "I have a rat down my cellar," I gasped.

"Yep," he said, "you'll get them in the cellar this time of year. Too much food outside for them to come up into your bedroom yet—in the daytime.

"Remember one time," he went on, "one leaped from the top of the kitchen door down my back." He spat out a piece of straw he'd been chewing and chuckled softly. "Thought I was going to lose him for a minute. Had to get my wife to hit me over the back with a broom."

A few days later we had a man doing odd jobs around the house. I told him about my rats. I told everybody about my rats. I couldn't stop talking about them. There wasn't a conversation I couldn't bring around to rats. I told editors about them, and waitresses and bank managers, during that silence after I'd asked for a loan. Anyway, this man went down to the cistern celler and crawled into a dark hole, humming "Annie Laurie." He put his arm up a drain, chuckled and said, "That's the place where they're coming from all right. Still warm in there. All you have to do is nail a grid over it." I supported myself against the wall.

171

I've never seen him again. I'm just as glad. I'd have to tell him I wouldn't have gone near that hole without a squad car.

What I did do was study their tracks. Somehow I felt that as long as I knew where they were and where they were going, I was holding my own. I found I had other tracks—tracks of moles, deer mice, field mice and house mice. They must have held election parades under my kitchen every night. I got so interested in studying their ways that I temporarily forgot we were trying to get one another out of the house. I'd come down in the morning, go out into the woodshed, yawn, come back and say to my wife, "Moles are coming back," yawn again, go down cellar and start the pump, look at a bit of sand by the tank and say, "Deer mice here last night," come upstairs, have some coffee, go down to the cistern cellar, call up to my wife from far beneath her feet, "Heh, heh, here's a funny one. Rats missed an apple I threw here yesterday, field mice came in after it and got chased off by the wood mice." My wife started to call me Oogoorook.

The animals even began to interfere with my marriage. A couple of phoebes built a nest in our woodshed, and my wife and I began to watch them make their little home. But male birds, I found, never worked. The female would be lugging twigs and mud, working herself into a nervous breakdown, while the male teetered on a clothesline, practically blowing on his fingernails. My wife would stare at him and say, "I suppose he'll take all the credit for laying the eggs, too," and ask me when I was going to start disciplining the children. When he did sit on the nest, my wife would say, "Now isn't that just too bad that he has to stop ogling other little phoebes long enough to warm a couple of eggs," and start thinking of all the times I'd been late getting back from the city.

If it had kept up much longer I would have been writing to a marriage counselor telling him I was having trouble with a phoebe. As it was, the end came soon after the eggs hatched and the five young ones developed flight feathers. I'd got into the habit of reaching up and tickling their little heads with my finger to see them open their mouths. One morning I did this when, without my knowing it, they were almost ready to fly, and they all took off in different directions. Our four cats and two neighbors' dogs, who began to chase the cats, appeared just as a man drove up to the farmhouse to try to sell me a full set of the *Encyclopedia Britannica*. The man looked at me as if considering reporting me to the Humane Society. By that time I was about ready to report the birds and all my other little furred and feathered friends.

Another thing, I was never quite able to get used to bulls—and by that I mean steers, heifers, bullocks and yearlings—they're all bulls to me unless they have sway-backs and obviously give lots of milk. The things used to draw me in fascinated horror. The barnyard was just a short piece from the house. I'd go out in the moonlight, and the herd and I would stand looking at one another, the steam coming up from the cows as the moon cast its magic over us. There was a brown one with a head like a teapot who was always staring at me over the backs of the others, like some guy in a crowd who thought I was someone who'd given him a bum check years ago.

Every now and then one of them would get into our

garden, and the farmer would come over to herd them back. He'd say, "You just stand there so he can't get past you." I used to wonder if the cow really thought it couldn't get past me, or whether animals actually were that dumb.

"Never let them know you're afraid of them," he'd say, walking up and giving him a cut over the sirloin with a rope and saying, "GIT out of there." He'd turn to me, "Remember, he's more afraid of you than you are of him," not knowing that nothing could be that afraid and keep eating.

In fact it was a cow that finally crystallized my growing conviction that life on the farm, although desirable in many ways, was not the right one for us. More exactly, it was a combination of a cow, a lollypop, and a partridge—or rather, what I *thought* was a partridge.

One of the reasons I'd chosen this farm to rent was that a good friend of mine—an ardent hunter—lived in the neighboring village. I'd never been much for the outdoor life, but instead of admitting frankly when I came to the country that the closest I'd ever come to partridge was in the bedtime stories of Thornton W. Burgess, I met all remarks about partridge shooting with the statement that I didn't have my gun with me, implying that I had a whole arsenal coming by train. As a result, I suddenly found myself sitting in a car with my friend, on my way to the woods. He had generously offered to let me use his gun on every other partridge.

He explained that he usually had his dog with him, but that today the dog was off somewhere with his sons. I made the mistake of saying that I'd be glad to help any way I could.

"I tell you what we'll do then," he said. "I'll head up

that hill. You go in there and follow along parallel to the road."

I looked to see where he had pointed and turned back to him ready to join in a good laugh. But he wasn't even smiling. I looked again. It was the sort of place where you might throw an old pop bottle, or perhaps a body. It was not a place to go in unless you were being followed by bloodhounds. But on the other side of the road, where my friend was going, there was a herd of cows, and there was something about walking through a herd of silent cows (if they *were* cows) and pretending they were just lucky that I didn't pick up a stick and whack them that left me shaking for a week. I headed for the bush.

We'd arranged a system of whistles. I was to whistle once just to let my friend know where I was, so that he wouldn't shoot me, which struck me as a sound idea, and twice if I saw a partridge. I climbed over a snake fence, disappeared momentarily down a ditch, reappeared covered with burs, faced a solid wall of small trees, pried two of them apart and found myself in a dense grove of dead cedars.

I started looking for partridge. I wasn't quite sure how you looked for them, but I imagined that you did it much the same way you'd look for anything else, like a fountain pen or a quarter, and that, in view of the position of the branches, it was done in about the same position. I took my glasses off so that they wouldn't get whipped from my face, and, whistling at intervals, like a toy locomotive in a Christmas display, started off like a man who has had a safe dropped on him.

I'd had enough experience with the sort of people who go in for hunting and fishing to know that they usually ate a quick breakfast before dawn and forgot about food until eight in the evening, and this time, just as we had been driving out of the village, I had asked my friend to stop while I got some cigarettes at a small country store. While in the tobacco stand, I had cased it quickly for something to eat. The selection hadn't been very good, and it ended with me passing up bubble gum and blackballs and, in desperation, taking a lollypop, raspberry flavor. I felt too silly about it to bring my friend one too and just slipped it into my pocket in a wax-paper bag. It was while I was sneaking my first lick, crouched there on all fours amid the cedars, that things began to happen.

Anyone who doesn't wear glasses mightn't quite understand how it's possible to mistake a cow for a partridge. But anyone with eyes like mine knows that there's a strong psychological factor in vision. What you see has a lot to do with what you expect to see. I know that one time in Toronto I waved traffic to a halt for two blocks while I ran to the rescue of what I thought was a hit-and-run victim and found myself walking sheepishly back to the curb with an empty coal sack that had fallen off a truck, while three lanes of motorists honked at me and a few drivers jeered. In the same way, a cow's foot, moving and rustling stealthily when the rest of the cow is camouflaged by trees, shadows and myopic mirages, looked pretty gamy.

I got pretty excited. I froze, raised my nose and pointed. I almost tried wagging my tail until I remembered the signal. I whistled twice, felt much better and began softly humming "Shrimp Boats" and waiting for the explosion of my friend's gun, licking my lollypop out of pure nervous reflex.

I hadn't discerned that I'd been approaching a clearing.

176

I certainly hadn't noticed the farmer who, I realized later, must have been standing there peering at me in some alarm from between the trees. The first I knew of him, his nerves finally cracked, and he called to the cow, "GIT out of there."

I screamed, sprang, whistled twice in mid-air and crashed headlong through a dead cedar into a patch of brambles. I poked my head up over the brambles and saw the whole situation with one horrified glance, while the farmer watched me, pale beneath his sunburn.

"Thought that was a partridge," I said, pointing to the cow.

The farmer backed off, holding a pitchfork toward me.

"Nice weather we're having, isn't it?" I said.

"Yep," the farmer said, still backing off.

"I guess you farmers could use a bit of rain, though," I said, coming out from the brambles, my pants making ripping sounds. I held out my lollypop, laughed and said, "Picked this up for lunch."

Just then my friend arrived, his gun over his arm, and said to me, "You got away from me." I saw the farmer turn and head for his house and the phone.

We didn't get any partridge, and we went home pretty soon after that. My friend never mentioned the incident. The next time he went partridge-shooting, he took his dog.

For weeks after, I noticed local people driving past my house slowly on Sunday afternoons, looking up, saying a few words and driving on. One day when I was buying some cigarettes, I overheard someone whisper, as if referring to a well-known event, "There's the city fella Jeff's brother came across that day down in his lower sixth."

Not that they didn't finally come around to recognizing me as a fairly normal human; in fact several of the farmers and villagers became my very good friends. But I never quite got over the feeling that it was a friendship of people who, however well disposed toward one another, lived in different worlds.

FOR some reason that I can't figure out to this day, in our search for the Perfect Place to Live, a search begun with a desire for sunshine and warmth, we had included a move that surrounded us with more snow than we'd seen before in our lives. Theoretically the country doesn't get more snow than the city, but as far as I'm concerned, this remains a theory. Every time we had a date, some important shopping to do or anything urgent to take care of, we got stuck in our driveway, which was built on a peculiar slant, so that as soon as I stepped on the gas, the car gaily waved its rear end and did a slow samba into a frozen cornfield.

At least once a week my wife and I sat in the front seat, all dressed up for the evening and smelling of shaving lotion and My Sin, sinking closer and closer to the ground as the car churned its way through the frozen corn stalks and settled down on its chassis. While I sat there dully spinning the wheels, my wife would go into the house and reappear looking like the leader of a peasants' revolt, carrying the coal shovel and the snow shovel, and we'd start to dig a big clear space. When we were finished, we'd lean on our shovels for a minute, then I'd get behind the wheel. The car would edge toward the new space slowly, then leap at it with a hoarse roar of delight and settle down again like an old hippo that's found a new water hole.

We'd keep this up, trying all sorts of devices, until a neighboring farmer, having heard the commotion, came over with his tractor, pulled the car back on the driveway and drove away chuckling to his chores. We were left standing amid the wreckage of churned-up chunks of frozen mud, coal sacks, sand, ashes, planks and shovels, feeling like having a hot bath and going to bed.

I started leaving the car down by the mailbox, an eighth of a mile from the house, so that I'd be close to the snow-plowed country road. The plow would dump all the snow on top of my car. Sometimes by the time I had shoveled a path up to the scene, dug the car out and cleared the way to the road, it would be snowing again and gaining on me.

The snow disappeared in late March. We put away our tire chains, snow shovels, mittens and overshoes. The robins came back in April. Right after that, the snow came back. It sneaked in sideways one night, whispering, blowing parallel to the ground and sticking to tree trunks, brick walls and windshields, and in the morning everything had been transformed to a winter wonderland. The snow even stuck to the robins. We had one sitting on a nest outside our glassed-in porch. She sat there, a true product of instinct, sitting on her eggs on schedule, wearing her layer of snow like a nightcap and bed jacket and looking a bit like a startled old lady sitting up in bed listening to the sound of passing hotrods. We looked each other in the eye, me inside the porch and her outside it, but both of us were thinking of the same thing—the South.

My wife and I finally decided that life on the farm wasn't for us. We had never really decided to *stay* on the farm, when you got right down to it. We'd come there really as a sort of trial. We were lucky, we told ourselves with feeble smiles, that we were free to live wherever we wanted to live. Most people couldn't move around the way we did. I mean, if I worked for a bank or someplace like that, we would just have to be satisfied with whatever place we were in. The oftener we said this, the more we wished I worked for a bank, where I wouldn't have to decide between several hundred places we hadn't lived yet.

Our arguments now took on a new, crisp decisiveness. We were very clear-headed about it. This moving around back and forth was ridiculous. Friends were beginning to

181

greet us, when we met them in Toronto, with, "Let's see, where are you living now?" We wanted to settle down, to have a home of our own. If we still wanted to travel after that, we wanted to be able to leave our books, pajamas, toys, tools and sewing baskets right where they were, waiting for us in the same place when we came back again.

We started bending down our fingers vigorously in each other's directions as we counted off the facts. We wanted a warm climate. We wanted one that was comfortable and livable year-round, with lots of sun, not too much humidity and just a normal quota of bugs. We wanted to stay among English-speaking people, preferably on this continent. We wanted the facilities of a city life.

We were a bit startled, halfway through the flurry of facts and finger bending, to find ourselves getting closer and closer to describing California. I recalled a conversation I'd had under a desert moon one night with a man from Cleveland, just before leaving for the coast on the first leg of our trip back home.

"Why go all the way back to Canada," he said, "then have to come all the way back here? It's expensive, moving around like that."

"What do you mean, come back?" I figured he'd been only half-listening.

"*Everybody* comes back to California."

"Look, you don't understand. I'm going back home, for good."

"*Everybody* goes back home for good. I've gone back home for good three times myself. We all come back to California within a year. Why don't you be smart and stay the first time?"

I hadn't mentioned it to my wife. It had seemed too

ridiculous. I didn't mention it now, either. In fact, neither my wife nor I mentioned California at all. We just went around humming absently, "California, Here I Come."

Then one noon hour out on the front lawn, when we were having a lunch of tea and sardine sandwiches, I put my head back on my deck chair, looked up at the sky and said, "Remember how blue the sky was in the desert?"

My wife looked over the cedar hedge toward the southwest and said thoughtfully, "And the flowers in Pasadena?"

"And the smell of the sea and hamburgs at Ocean Park?"

"And the Good Humor Man?"

"And the beer cans on the highways?"

"And the seal with the bad eye at Santa Monica?"

"And the parkfull of bums in Los Angeles?"

"And the supermarkets?"

"And the day we saw Jane Russell?"

By the time we finished the last sardine sandwich, we'd made up our minds. When we told the kids about it after school, they began packing their possessions. By suppertime they were sitting out in the car ready to go. I explained that it would take a couple of months.

Six weeks later, applying for a visa again, since ours had lapsed, I appeared at the same old Consulate steps in Toronto, lugging my file of material. I walked up to the desk, saw the same young man, a bit older, locked eyes with him for a moment and opened my mouth to speak. Slowly, without taking his eyes off me, he motioned with his pencil to the benches.

"Just sit down, please."

But I got another visa without any trouble. Two days later we sent our furniture off to storage, planning to send for it from California. We had used it for a while, anyway.

183

By noon we had mopped up the floor, checked the clothes closets, left the key for the new tenant with a neighbor and loaded the car ready to go.

The car looked like the inside of a moving van. We had made a rule that Mary and Jane could each have a carton in the back seat and take along enough of her stuff to fill it, but no more. They'd had a contest to see who could think up the most ingenious way of beating the rules. They had turned the flaps up on the cartons and bound them with skipping ropes and had managed to pile each one almost up to the dome lights. Both kids took up a lot more of the back seat themselves than they had on the first trip. Everybody sat in a little nest, surrounded by cartons, bags, clothes and books. My wife and I had to take more stuff in between us on the front seat, so that when we wanted to exchange flight information, we had to crane our necks to see each other.

The trunk was even worse. I had coat hangers, roller skates, a steam iron, bumper jack, cross wrench and two volumes of Plato behind the spare tire and everything I owned in front of it, in cartons, bundles and our sad, battered old luggage which I had intended to make do until I could afford a couple of really good sets right after our honeymoon. When I thought of having to change a tire, the only solution I could find was just to stop thinking about it.

Just as I had the trunk packed so that I had to take a run, spin around in mid-air and sit on the door to close it, Mary appeared from somewhere with a big, hulking, unco-operative old bag of a doll, about the size and shape of a dinghy. I couldn't have fitted it in if I'd put it through a garbage-disposal unit, and don't think I wouldn't have. She hadn't

184

played with it for years, and, as far as I knew, never even thought of it. But it evidently had some strange, powerful attachment for her and represented home, and she stood there with her face flushed, ready to turn the whole incident into a traumatic experience that would spread from Toronto to Tombstone, Arizona, if I didn't get it in the car.

I finally gave up and got the doll in by emptying a few cartons and distributing the contents around in little spare holes and cracks in the trunk, hoping I wouldn't have to open it until I smelled the Pacific.

My wife made a last-minute check of the glove compartment, arranging maps, pencils, facecloths, clothespins (my wife always took clothespins along with her, probably for the same reason that Mary took her doll), peppermint sticks, flashlight, carsick pills, cold cream, credit card, paper cups, baking soda, bottle opener and a couple of dusters. I let the clutch out, and we rolled down the driveway.

"Good-by, house," I said flatly, beginning the formula again.

"Do you think I'll be able to study French in California?" Jane asked.

"Good-by, lawn," I persisted.

"Did you put Mary's pills in that carton with the sandwiches?" my wife said. She looked up. "Good-by, lawn," she said conversationally, then turned back to Jane and said, "I told you not to wear that blouse."

"Good-by, driveway," I said absently through the windshield.

"Good-by," Mary said mechanically. "I hope we get one of those motor courts with TV."

15

I BECAME forty on our trip to California. It took me completely by surprise. Not that I hadn't known all along that it would happen—after all, I'd been thirty-nine

186

for a year. But the difference between knowing you're thirty-nine and suddenly realizing you're forty is the difference between hearing the dentist say over the phone that he can take you a week from next Thursday and hearing him say around his door, "Ps-s-s-t! You're next."

I became forty one night when I was standing beside a neon motel sign having a last cigarette, watching the cars hum down the highway, each one leaving me with my pants flapping, listening to the silence, broken only by the sound of crickets and the buzz of the neon sign. The sound of the sign reminded me of one time a few years before when I'd started a chemistry course at night school, had got as far as the inert gases, which I'd memorized as "krypton, argon, neon and so-on," and had dropped the whole idea of being a chemist, as I'd dropped a lot of things in my life. It suddenly occurred to me that in a few days I would be forty.

It struck me as about the dirtiest trick I'd ever had played on me. Being forty was something that happened to schoolteachers, aunts, elephants, character actors, fathers, streetcar motormen and people who dropped dead shoveling snow. It had never had anything to do with me. I had been about twenty-seven for years. I still was, somehow. The person who had changed was some character who peered out of motel mirrors at me when I shaved.

Along with my face, quite a few things outside me had changed. My kids were growing about two inches a day, and I'd stopped wondering whether I should lick them and had started to wonder whether I *could* lick them. When I tried to terrify them into obedience, I caught that look in their eyes that I used to get in mine as a boy, when some old gentleman started after me for ringing his doorbell and tripped on the little wire around his geraniums.

187

At forty, other men had made their mark on the world. I hadn't even found the right place to live yet. Instead of doing the sorts of things that writers are supposed to do, like going to pieces in Paris with a beautiful blonde, I was falling apart slowly from the vibration on the highways. I didn't have a home of my own, and I was as undignified by age as I'd been at seventeen. And I realized that if I were going to find the Perfect Place to Live and still have time to settle down and do a few things I wanted to do, I'd just about have time for this one last crack at it. It was all a little like coming out of a movie about a South Sea island and finding that it had been raining outside and turning to sleet. Life may begin at forty; the joker is that you're forty just when it's beginning. It's like discovering a clunk in the rear end of a car you haven't had a chance to drive yet.

Something similar had been happening to my wife. We were both conscious that we weren't traveling: we were moving again, in a businesslike frame of mind that distinguished us from most people on the road, who are usually in an expansive, holiday mood. We treated expenses with a matter-of-fact objectivity and complete indifference to the impression we made on fellow travelers, who were all trying to look well-heeled. We'd walk into a restaurant in the morning, half-asleep and preoccupied with our affairs, and look at the menu. If the prices were too high, we'd all get up and file out, as silently as a family of Plains Indians, past the cashier and the hostess, who exchanged puzzled looks. This sort of thing didn't embarrass the kids; they were used to it. Often they walked in still reading their books and walked out still reading them, so that we looked as if half the family were at morning vespers.

It was the same when we started off for the day's drive.

Instead of gay preparations, lively consultations about routes and discussions about all the interesting places we were going to see, we just yawned and headed the car in the general direction of the southwest. Around noon, my wife would fish an old road map out from behind some face-cloths to make sure we hadn't made any wrong turns. If we got off our route in a city, instead of flurried consultations of tour books, we just circled around looking at the buildings until we recognized the highway we'd been on.

On the way I automatically talked about the Perfect Place to Live with anyone who felt like talking about it, and a lot did. We weren't the only ones looking for it. I found that the desire to find the Perfect Place to Live is a frame of mind that came in with rapid transportation. It has made a lot of people restless to find a better place than the one they are in. Everybody has a different idea of where it is.

I talked to a big, handsome, sloppy-looking, red-headed girl who operated a motor court in the desert and who wanted to go to some place like Pennsylvania, where you could see leaves, although her husband wanted to go to Mexico.

One morning I stood in the office of a motor court where they served free coffee to their guests, trying to wake up and talking to a middle-aged couple from Brockville, Ontario. The woman said her idea of California was sand, oil wells and beer cans and that the real place to live was Florida. Her husband scowled at her over his coffee and said he thought Florida was a place of bugs, heat and humidity, and California a place of mountains, sparkling seas and clear blue skies.

Another hardy, boisterous gray-haired executive with an

oil company told me happily that he'd been moved back to Chicago, where he could see snow again, after ten years in Long Beach. The only ones who didn't like it were his wife and three daughters. He drew me aside and told me confidentially that the reason women liked living in the south was that they could "slop around in beach clothes." He looked toward the north and said, "Me, I like to wear a suit."

One morning before we left a motor court, I got to talking to a chirpy, attractive, dark-eyed girl from the East about the route I should follow out of town. She told me to take the next turn to the left and held out her right hand. When I said, "You mean right," she said, "I mean left," waved her right arm again, laughed and said, "Where've you been?" I said it must have been somewhere different than the place she'd been, because that still looked like her right hand. She started to wave it again, realized her mistake and told me that she was from Brooklyn, on her way to make her home in Texas, and was already so homesick that it was a wonder that she knew up from down.

We had a blowout somewhere around Yuma, out among the sand dunes. I had to unload the whole trunk, starting with Mary's doll and ending up with my wife's steam iron. I stacked the stuff along the edge of the highway. Looking at all your possessions lying in a heap in the bright desert sun is an experience that makes you realize with crystal clarity your position in the social scale. We looked like a family of old-time medicine-show tumblers who had just been run out of town, and when I had the tire fixed, I tried to overcome the impression by taking the kids and walking back over the sand dunes until the car and the highway were out of sight.

When I came back, I found my wife talking to a couple from Albany, New York, who had stopped to see if she needed any help. We found that they were moving to Arizona to live but weren't quite sure that it was the right place and wondered whether the ideal place mightn't lie somewhere halfway between the north and the south, like Carmel, California. The man stood there, wearing a dark, northern-looking suit and vest, a hat and glasses, looking thoughtfully over the dunes and wondering if he could stand Christmas without snow.

The day before Christmas the kids picked some kind of little cactus plant beside the highway and rigged it up for a Christmas tree in the back seat of the car. They cut out decorations from magazines and pinned them by strings to the top of the car. We had done some of our Christmas shopping before leaving Canada and the rest along the road. Christmas Eve we stopped early in a dingy little western town and piled our presents around the five-inch cactus Christmas tree in the corner of the room. I had bought four Cokes at fifteen cents each from a woman behind one of the shabbiest little bars I'd ever seen, with two well-primed cowhands standing on either side of me, beating out the rhythm of a tune on the juke box by slapping the bar as if it were a pony's haunches.

I expected the worst when we went into one of the town's two restaurants for supper. As often happens, we had one of the best meals I've ever eaten, served in surroundings as dainty as an Eastern tea shop, at prices so reasonable that my wife and I spent about half the meal trying to figure out how they could do it and make a profit. During the whole meal another cowboy, who had evidently been riding the magic carpet all afternoon, sat beaming at us steadily and happily out of a ruddy, merry face with a broken nose. He was joined later by a sober friend, and when my wife and the kids got up and went into the washroom, I got talking to them. The sober one told me that he'd been a cattle hand all his life until a year ago, when he'd found he could make more money driving a school bus.

Christmas morning my wife and I lay in bed watching the kids open their presents then opened our own, toasted each other with orange juice from a can we'd bought the night before, and by six-thirty were driving out of the sleeping town toward a pink range of mountains, listening to the kids sing duets of Christmas carols and feeling very strange.

Two days later we reached the coast and began looking for our permanent home. We still had one detail to decide —just where we were going to live in California, a state approximately nine hundred miles long by three hundred wide. We got a map of California from a filling station, parked outside a drugstore in Pasadena and started to pick out our future home.

We were able to eliminate large sections without even looking up from the map. We had been told by many people that San Francisco was one of the most picturesque and cosmopolitan centers in the United States, but everyone added that there was a lot of fog there. We decided that if we were going to live someplace where the sun was blotted out for long periods, we could have done just as well in Toronto, which we'd left in order to get more sunshine. We had been told of various districts around San Francisco that the fog missed, but we didn't feel that we wanted to shave things that close. The whole northern part of California, in fact, although we'd been told many times that it was among the world's most beautiful areas, just didn't seem to figure into our original conception of a move to the South.

We eliminated other vast areas of California simply by deciding that we didn't want to live in the desert or the mountains, one being too hot, and the other getting too much snow. Anyway, we didn't want to live in the wilderness. But when you eliminate the wilderness from California, and I hope nobody ever does, you're left with a relatively thin strip of coast. We decided that we'd have to explore this for ourselves. We headed for the coast highway.

During the next five days we toured the coast from Santa Barbara to the Mexican border, with zigzags inland, but mentally we were flying in ever-decreasing circles around the Los Angeles area. Santa Barbara was beautiful but, from our point of view, too small. In fact, there were a lot of picturesque little places up and down the coast, but we had decided when we were on the farm in Canada that we didn't want any more little places; we wanted a great big place. At least we wanted one within an hour or an hour-and-a-half drive from the city.

Places like Riverside and San Bernardino seemed about right in many respects, but, although we wanted the sun in the winter, we didn't want to be roasted in summer, and we preferred to be within easy reach of the sea. San Diego struck us as a real contender for the Perfect Place, but all we knew about it was what we saw driving through Balboa park and stopping to look at the gorillas and koalo bears, which isn't any way to judge a city. Faced with the actual prospect of exploring a big, strange city and deciding whether it would be suitable for a permanent home, at the end of a 3,500-mile drive with all your bags in the car is

193

just one of those things that seem logical only at a distance of 3,500 miles. We had a picnic lunch within calling distance of the monkeys and headed north up the coast again.

So we arrived, as we had felt we would all along, in the Los Angeles area. But Los Angeles is a big place and takes in everything from settings for bloody detective stories to places like Beverly Hills, where I couldn't have afforded the down payment on some of the shrubs. I had only one experience with Beverly Hills. For the sake of the kids I paid an old gentleman a dollar for a map to the homes of the movie stars and found myself looking for Tony Curtis' house among a bunch of oil wells and fender shops. That old guy must have made his maps from a chamber of commerce catalogue of available industrial sites. When I finally got back to Beverly Hills, I had to turn around by backing into the driveway of a house that had been imported brick by brick from the Scotch highlands. I dug my drooping exhaust pipe into some imported cobblestones with sound effects that brought a couple of imported gardeners up off their knees and slowed down a patrol car of Beverly Hills cops, who circled around the block eying me as if they were shooting a scene for a television mystery.

We made a tour of the real estate offices in Santa Monica. We were shown one dark house by a tall, friendly real estate man who explained some oil stains on the wall, smiled at us through the gloom of the house and said it could be made to look very cheery with a bit of imagination. We thought that in its present condition it wasn't much of a buy at $9,000 and told him so when we got out on the street. He looked at us queerly and told us quietly that he had said nine*teen* thousand dollars and that he doubted if we could buy a lot in that area for $9,000.

When I left one real estate office, I was followed to the door by a brisk, seedy-looking old gentleman, who motioned me around a corner and said that he hadn't wanted to say anything inside the real estate office, but that he thought he could be of some help to us. It all hinged somehow on driving him to downtown Los Angeles, and the more he talked, the more vague he became about what he was going to do for us and the more clear-headed about the part where we drove him downtown.

The car was already so loaded with my luggage and my family that it looked as if it had no back wheels, and I finally told him that I was really too crowded to give him a lift. We parted on the best of terms, with him waving and saying, "You'll like it in Santa Monica. I've lived here for thirty years, and I wouldn't live any other place in the world. But you've got to watch them. They'll steal the gold fillings right out of your teeth."

I nodded and waved and started back to the car. He called to me again and added, "Then after they stole 'em, they'd sell 'em back to you."

I smiled and nodded and kept going. He called happily from a distance, "They'd steal your *teeth* if they could get them loose."

When I finally drove off, I passed him on the corner, and he called through the window merrily, "Steal your mother's fillings, too."

I grinned and waved. He waved back. "Steal their *own* mother's fillings," he called from far off.

I headed south down the coast, with him still calling faintly about fillings.

We got lost that evening among the oil wells of Venice, and by the time we got back to the highway were determined to get farther south still and running out of ideas about where we were going to settle.

But we found the place the next morning. A small town on the ocean, within less than an hour's drive from downtown Los Angeles, set on the blue Pacific on the side of a mountain, surrounded by avacado groves and a really beautiful setting of roof tops, trees and the sea. It looked like the Perfect Place to Live.

For the time being, we rented a place that looked like a movie-producer's beach house. We started the kids at school and I settled down to getting some articles done, including one that I'd started on the farm back in Canada on the importance of the pig on the Canadian farm. I was probably the only writer on the west coast, and probably always will be, who sat in a beach house looking out over the Pacific, surrounded by the smell of the sea, charcoal-broiled steaks and eucalyptus trees, writing about pigs.

The day I finished the pig article, I got in the car and drove to Hollywood to make a proper start as a west-coast writer. I stood at a noisy, crowded bar, feeling every inch a Hollywood character, watching men with cigars make phone calls from their lunch tables and call noisily to one another, "Are you shooting?" I was introduced to a lot of people, who all introduced me to someone who didn't want to meet me either.

Everybody handed me a card absently, looked over my head and hollered at someone, "Are you shooting?" We all stood around exchanging cards as if we were making change. Distinguished, silver-haired men told me jokes that used to make me puff excitedly on my willow leaves. One man, when I told him of a magazine article I had in mind, looked at me pointedly and said, "Screwballs arrive here by the busload." I wandered out into the Hollywood sunshine convinced that if I were going to do any writing in Hollywood, this wasn't the approach. I fingered the stack of cards I'd been given by men who had said, "My phone number is on that," and for one mad moment I thought I might get in a phone booth later on in the afternoon with a fistfull of dimes, call them all and ask them what they wanted.

I decided to go back to the beach and keep on writing non-Hollywood articles. I had other things on my mind—particularly one big thing—settling down finally in The Perfect Place.

16

I'M still settling down. Something new and strange has happened to us. We've found the Perfect Place to Live. For the first time in our married lives, we haven't any excuse for not being happy. We have no excuse about the weather. We have lots of sunshine, a dry, invigorating climate. We can wear summer clothes year-round. We're never uncomfortable. We never have to worry about bugs —there aren't any. We need a blanket at night. We've actually found the Perfect Place to Live. It's a bit unnerving.

I can see long vistas of contented years ahead with nothing to complain about. No longer will I be able to say, "Look at that dirty weather outside. No wonder a man can't get up any energy." I'll just have to say, "Another beautiful day, eh?" and get back to work.

The life before us is completely different from anything we've ever known. Before we came here, we were on the move for eight years. We never completely settled down mentally in any one place. There were always reservations. Implicit in any move was the thought that it would do until we found a better place. We led a nomadic existence, following the sun and our dreams. Now it's all over. The search has ended. We have found the pot of gold. We are sitting right inside the pot at the end of the rainbow, occasionally peering over the edge at our surroundings and biting our lips thoughtfully.

This place is the farthest you can get from the United States sociologically without leaving the continent. It's nobody's home town. It is populated by people who looked hard for it and found it. Nobody was born or raised here. Everybody moved here and hasn't had time to belong here yet. Some of them are going back home, and others are arriving breathlessly, so there's a brisk trade in real estate. Every house in town is for sale. You never ask a home owner whether he wants to sell his house, you ask him how

199

much he wants for it. It's understood that he'll sell it if he can see a chance of moving to a better place.

The cult of the Perfect Place has brought many pilgrims, all of the same secular faith, which expresses itself in many areas of life. In the Perfect Place to Live everything should be perfect, so the inhabitants just naturally correct things they didn't like about their home towns, like the names of stores and businesses which, on the Outside, are often very drab, if not downright vulgar. Here a grocery store is never just called Sam's Grocery. It's called The Eat Nook. If it's a wallpaper store, it's called the Paste Nook, and if it's a notions store, it's called The Button Hook.

I find myself in some strange bits of dialogue with my wife. I'll say, "Welp, I have to go downtown to do some shopping. I'm going to pick up some copy paper at the Treasure Trove and some paper clips at The Pirate's Cove, then drop in at the Painted Toadstool, take the car in to the Brake Hospital and leave it there for half an hour. I'll wait in the Grog and Smog."

"All right," my wife says, "but don't forget to pick up that parcel for me at the Stitch and Tuck."

Nobody just owns a dog. One owns a freshly trimmed French poodle, an Afghan, a Chihuahua or a champion Doberman, which all peer haughtily at one another around the eucalyptus trees. One old hound, who must have sneaked into town on a slow freight, comes rooting around our neatly tied garbage nosing for bones, and the other dogs just won't speak to him.

It's the most beautiful place we've ever seen. There are no ugly back fences. Houses are separated by trees and canyons, and all have a sweeping panorama of the Pacific. We often sit among our leaves looking at it and thinking how beautiful it is. Sometimes we think nostalgically of some

200

of the crummy places we've lived where people talked to one another over their ugly back fences. Occasionally, when I look at it too long, I begin to feel so detached from vulgar reality that I renew my contact with life by getting up, driving to Los Angeles and having lunch in a place I've found that serves wonderful bacon and eggs and is patronized almost exclusively by bums who still haven't found the Perfect Place to Live.

Now that I've found it myself, in fact, I'm not quite sure what to do with it. For years it has been my inclination to move to places that looked better than the one I was in. If I sat in a movie, for example, looking at a beautifully done technicolor travelogue of a Mediterranean village perched in the sun on the green hills, I thought something like, "What a beautiful place! Why live someplace where you have to do without all that? Maybe we should go there to live."

But thinking that you can just move right into beautiful scenes and live there is a lot like thinking that you should just sit in the movie forever. What gives distant places their appeal, although perfectly real and valid, doesn't have much weight when you get there. I don't mean what people mean when they say, "Maybe you don't get snow, but how about those earthquakes and rattlesnakes?" I'm not talking about the philosophy that there's something wrong with everyplace, which often isn't philosophy but just mental inertia.

There are a lot fewer things wrong with some places than others, and refusal to admit it often rests on the same psychological quirk that sometimes caused people who heard of our starting on a long trip to say anxiously, "What would

201

you do if the children got sick?" evidently figuring that doctors and hospitals were a local idea. All I'm saying is that the appeal of a distant and beautiful place loses its objectivity when you arrive there, and when it becomes subjective, it's a different thing. You can't sit on a hill overlooking the Pacific looking at the scenery all day, or you'll end up playing tic-tac-toe. You can't live with a picture postcard. You have to eat, talk, work, have interests and friends, feel at home, know your way around—in short, live, not just look and admire the weather.

I've found, too, that there's a vital psychological difference between visiting a place and settling down there permanently. I've often thought about someplace I've seen, "My gosh, why go home? This is terrific. I'm having a wonderful time here. Too bad I have to leave." But I'd have to leave, and I'd take my favorable impressions with me.

Suddenly I found myself *not* leaving one of these wonderful places. I stood looking at a strange place, settled down permanently at last, took a deep breath and said, "Welp! This is the place where I'm going to die." The minute I said it, I felt like dying immediately.

We often sit at supper in the soft glow of a big candle we bought in Tiajuana, and someone says, "Isn't it good to know that we don't have to move around any more? It's going to be wonderful to know that we can dig right in, for good."

Immediately everyone becomes silent, Mary thinking, I know, of the farmer who used to give her rides on the tractor, Jane thinking of the nights she used to skate on the pond behind our barn, my wife thinking of her friends in Ontario, and me looking out the window toward the Pacific, where the last light is fading from another perfect day, thinking of a restaurant in Toronto that I used to nip into on dark, sloppy mornings for coffee with about half a dozen of my cronies. I immediately forget what a perfect day it has been.

I've forgotten the weather for such long periods, in fact, that I think if I had my life to live over again, I'd forget the weather right from the beginning. I'd never give the weather a thought. I'd never look at a weather map or listen to a forecast, I'd never talk about the weather, look at the weather or think about the weather. When I began to feel cold, I'd put on fleece-lined mitts, long underwear, a scarf, sweaters and, if necessary, earmuffs and an electric de-froster. As the season drew to an end, and I began to feel too warm, I'd start taking them off. As long as my body temperature remained constant, I'd ignore what the tem-perature was outside me. I'd forget there was such a thing as climate.

Because once you start getting involved with the weather, it takes up too much of your life. You haven't that much time. I want to turn my attention to something more im-portant than spending my days peering at clouds and patches of fog and cold fronts and wondering which way they're going to move.

I know now that the way out of the predicament is to settle on one place and accept it—snow, frost, fog, smog or whatever goes with it. It's really an old story—the only way to get the best out of anything is to make the best of the good things you've got.

There's just one thing I'm not quite sure of: whether to

make the best of the good things I've got here or to go back and make the best of the good things I left.

EDITOR'S NOTE: When this manuscript went to press, the author and his family had started back to Toronto.